GW00500186

Chapters in the Life of
REX ROMAN

SIMON ASH

WISH YOU WERE HERE

Chapters in the Life of REX ROMAN

SIMON ASH

Chapters in the Life of Rex Roman
Copyright © 2008 Simon Ash
The moral right of the author has been asserted.

Apart from any fair dealing for the purposes of research or private study, or criticism or review, as permitted under the Copyright, Designs and Patents Act 1988, this publication may only be reproduced, stored or transmitted, in any form or by any means, with the prior permission in writing of the publishers, or in the case of reprographic reproduction in accordance with the terms of licences issued by the Copyright Licensing Agency. Enquiries concerning reproduction outside those terms should be sent to the publishers.

Lyrics by Roger Waters reproduced by kind permission of Warner Chappell.

Every effort has been made to trace copyright holders and we apologise in advance for any unintentional omission. We would be pleased to insert the appropriate acknowledgement in any subsequent edition.

Matador
9 De Montfort Mews
Leicester LE1 7FW, UK
Tel: (+44) 116 255 9311 / 9312
Email: books@troubador.co.uk
Web: www.troubador.co.uk/matador

ISBN 978-1906221-881

Cover artwork concept by Tina Lewis.
Cover digitally assembled by Andy Cross under duress in Simon's kitchen, with constant 'Is that proper red?...I don't do orangey-red,' comments from Tina.

Typeset by Andy Cross & Simon Ash.
Andy would like it to be known that it was Simon's idea to have complete disregard for any long standing typographical rules and protocols. He approached the typesetting like a complete barbarian, while Andy shook his head in disbelief.

Tina would also like it to be known that Simon ignored all of her sterling advice on the rules of grammar and punctuation.

Poster Design by Troubador Publishing Ltd, Leicester, UK.

Printed by TJ International, Padstow, Cornwall, UK.

Matador is an imprint of Troubador Publishing Ltd.

Contents in the Life of...

Contents in the Life of...

A Note From The Author

Rex Roman was first introduced to me in a restaurant, by a very attractive American TV executive, some years ago. She was quite lovely actually, but I digress...the point is that I liked Rex instantly and I soon discovered that we had three things in common. We were both British citizens overseas, we both had the chicken pasta and we both loved Pink Floyd.

As Rex is much older than me, I was fascinated to hear about his memories of the band and their musical influence in the 1970s.

I am, by trade, a professional session drummer. As I got to know Rex over the years, the moment Pink Floyd reformed I knew that it was a sign. I pitched the idea to Rex that we should write a musical about his life, set to the music of Pink Floyd.

We did just that. We wrote a full script, rearranged some of the classic Floyd songs to better fit the story and recorded the whole idea as an audio CD (never released). In the end, after much debate, we had 2hrs 10mins of pure entertainment.

Feeling positive about this, I went to dinner with a top lawyer and he depressed the life out of me with one word - *Copyright.* However, he did agree that Rex's story could be told - *In print.*

So, acting on that good advice, Rex & I set off for France in April, 2007. Once there, Rex began telling more of his hilarious stories as I took notes. The more he talked, the more I laughed and the time we spent together writing this book was one of the happiest and most creative periods of my life. I hope you enjoy reading it as much as we enjoyed writing it.

God bless you, Rex Roman.

Your friend
Simon Ash

THE REXASAURUS

Rex Roman is British, yet he lives in America. This book is about Rex and his life story. Therefore, some of the terms are relevant to both the location and the era.

The Rexasaurus is a reference guide, much like The Thesaurus, that will help you to understand some of the Rexisms and sometimes bizarre language contained within this book. It is here to further aid your enjoyment of the next 43 chapters and to enlighten you about various strange words/phrases, you may or may not be familiar with.

You thought this book was the definitive guide to the rock group Pink Floyd? Oops, did you not read the bit on the back cover?

You hate Pink Floyd? Why??? Well, good news, you can enjoy this book even if you don't like the band. However, if you are a fan then you will discover the best-kept secret in rock history.

DON'T READ THE REXASAURUS NOW!!!

You might spoil your own fun. BUT, remember it's all here at the front, in chapter related order, just in case you become confused by a phrase during your read.

For the most enjoyment, skip the next few pages, turn to the first page of Chapter 1 and get started...

Your journey through time awaits you...

Go on, off you go...enjoy yourself.

P.S. Try and avoid looking at the back pages as some extra Rex related treats are there, all best kept secret until the end.

THE REXASAURUS

Term ✍	Definition ✍
Chapter 1	
Aura	*Vibe / Atmosphere*
Well-heeled	*Rich*
Jolly	*Happy*
Jaunt	*Trip*
Jolly Jaunt	*Happy trip*
Aka	*Also known as*
Razzmatazz	*Showbiz glamour*
UK	*United Kingdom (Northern Ireland, Scotland, England, Wales)*
Britain or Great Britain	*Scotland, England & Wales*
Un café-crème	*French for: A milky coffee*
S'il vous plait	*Please (French for: If you please – literal translation)*
Leg end	*Idiot*
Stinker	*Rubbish, really bad*
Vive la France	*Long live France*
Zat *(French accent)*	*That*
Pop his clogs	*Die*
Bean Counter	*Accountant*
In tatters	*In shreds, ruined*
Aah	*Exclamation used to express a favourable idea (dream / ideal)*
Holy Moly	*Daft expression of surprise*
Crikey	*Expression of surprise*
Everyone & their dog	*Lots of people*
Chapter 2	
Guffaws	*Term for laughter*
Buttock	*Join two together to form one bum or arse / ass*

Chapter 2 (Cont)

Oi	*Used to attract someone's attention in a rough way*
Bananas	*Crazy*
Mirth	*Amusement*

Chapter 3

Ribbing	*Teasing*
Wooing	*Charming, romantically speaking*
The Lothario swine	*Jestful term of jealously as Bradley is popular with the girls*
Alreet noo, that'll dee far the day *(Geordie accent)*	*Alright now, that will do for today (In Geordie, the language of those folks from the glorious town of Newcastle, England)*

Chapter 4

Gnashers	*Teeth (set of)*
Mom *(American version)*	*Mum*

Chapter 5

Chez Milwee	*House of Milwee (Bradley's home)*
Chez Roman	*House of Roman (Rex's home)*
PBJ	*Peanut Butter & Jelly, a classic sandwich treat*
Chips	*The American word for British crisps*
Jelly	*The American word for British jam*
Smackers	*Money / Pound notes*

Chapter 6

Damn Limeys	*Americans often call British people 'Limeys'. Derived from Admirals giving their sailors 'limes' to prevent illness from scurvy (circa 18th century)*
Scant	*Little / Small*
Popped out on stalks	*Expression of amazement*
Hon	*Short for 'Honey'*

Chapter 7	
Wot you bin sayin? *(London accent)*	*What you been saying?*
Filffy *(London accent)*	*Filthy*
Bee in his bonnet	*(Gary is) Obsessed with an idea*
Wiv *(London accent)*	*With*
Baying mob	*Assembled crowd howling for a fight*
Hangdog	*Downcast, guilty in appearance*
You betcha *(U.S. expression)*	*Yes, you can bet on it*

Chapter 8	
Tightwad	*Tight with your wad of money – tightwad. Mean with money*
Yummy	*Delicious*
Faux pas *(French phrase)*	*Social blunder, gaffe*

Chapter 9	
Taking the mickey	*To mock someone*
Serious pasting	*To give someone a good beating*

Chapter 12	
Ding-a-ling	*Sound of a bell ringing. Although Chuck Berry had a different idea*
Nerd	*Can be a fool or someone that is a single minded expert*
Smug	*Having excessive pride in oneself*
Ooh	*Exclamation used to express excitement for something*
Nasty niff	*Bad smell*

Chapter 13	
The Wombles	*Stop-motion childrens programme. No one knows if they are hedgehogs, bears or genius fiction. Living in a family group on Wimbledon Common, Great Uncle Bulgaria is the chief Womble*

Chapter 13 (Cont)

Stop-motion	*Technique used by animators i.e. Wallace & Gromit*
Goody bag	*Bag containing good stuff to eat, such as fairy cakes*
Packing under a coat	*Carrying a gun under a coat*
Lightweight	*Implies someone is weak*
Pungent stench	*Bad smell*

Chapter 14

Gigantic whopper	*Big lie, nothing to do with burgers*
Plonker	*Idiot, in an endearing way*

Chapter 15

Au naturel *(French phrase)*	*Naturally - as in the cereal straight out of the box in this case*
Soggy	*Wet and soft – when applied to toast it's horrible*
Just not cricket	*Just not right*
Beeline	*The most direct route between two places (i.e. Rex & Hot Dog)*
Glee	*Joy*
Wiv *(London accent)*	*With*
Lah-di-dah	*Expressing derision at someone's pretentious manner or speech*
Splat	*Sound of something wet hitting a surface*
Swig	*Mouthful*
Bonnet	*Car hood that covers the engine*
Banging on and on	*Continuously talking*

Chapter 16

Jammy devil	*Someone that's very lucky*
Dapper	*Well dressed*
Rendezvous	*French for: Meeting place*

Chapter 16 (Cont)

Panto	*Short for 'pantomime'. A British theatre tradition popular at Christmas time, mainly for children*

Chapter 17

Winner	*Good idea*
Peck on the cheek	*Small kiss on the cheek*

Chapter 18

Smacker	*Kiss*
Crikey	*Expression of surprise*
Playing a blinder	*Good performance / smart move*
Well-oiled	*Drunk*

Chapter 19

Close, but no cigar	*Failed at the last step*
Blighty	*Britain (Slang term for Britain)*
Top-drawer move	*Good idea*
Flatliner	*No pulse / Dead*
Tummy	*Stomach*

Chapter 20

Coughing up a gold watch	*Serious cough (smoker's cough / coughing fit)*
Disco	*Nightclub / Style of music*

Chapter 21

Scorcher	*Really hot*
Outback Aussie	*The kind of Australian that lives in the bush away from civilisation*
Earshot	*Range of hearing*
Chestnut of a gag	*Good joke*
Frenzy	*Heightened state of excitement*
Antipodean	*Inhabitants of Australia and New Zealand*

Chapter 22

Thespian wave	*Roll your hand as you bow*

Chapter 23

Huff and puff	*Sulk or moan*
Guv'ner / Guv'nor	*The Boss*
Gag	*Joke*
The Sweeney	*Popular 70s cop show about London's Flying Squad*
Aka	*Also known as*
Ding Dong	*Fight or argument*
Rex World	*A deluded, harmless place where the inhabitants live in a perpetual state of child-like creative fun* (*Currently has population of one: Rex!*)

Chapter 24

Le grand fromage	*French for: The big cheese*

Chapter 25

Rod Hull & Emu	*One man (Rod Hull) with a large blue puppet Emu stuck on his arm. Rod used his arm as the bird's neck and beak. Genius!*
A bit peaky	*Looking ill / off colour*
Woof down / (wolf down)	*Eat quickly*

Chapter 26

Gute Fahrt	*German for: Good / safe trip. Rex heard it as "good fart"*

Chapter 27

Egg laying	*Where you lay seeds and hope they grow into bigger things*
Watering holes	*Pubs / Bars*
Tipple	*Drink*

Chapter 28

Off like a rocket	*Leave at great speed*
Whopper	*Big*
Porker	*Pig or a lie*

Chapter 29

Fetching	*Attractive*
Speedos	*Popular brand of swimming trunks. (Often used for budgie smuggling)*

Chapter 30

Kudos	*Credibility*
Smorgasbord	*Selection of / a variety, usually associated with food buffet*
Trill	*Budgie / bird food*
Ambience soaking	*Magical time at a venue before the show actually starts*
In a pickle	*Faced with a dilemma / problem*
Crooner	*A singer, typically a male, who sings sentimental nonsense*

Chapter 31

Yow'll loik this one *(Brummie/Birmingham accent)*	*You will like this one (Slick!)*
Big girl's blouse	*Derogatory comment to imply someone is less than manly*

Chapter 33

Cheese slid off of their crackers	*Description of madness*
Dab hand	*To be good at something*
Vill *(German accent)*	*Will*
Viz *(German accent)*	*With*

Chapter 36

LAX	*Los Angeles International Airport*

Chapter 37

Chug	*Swig / mouthfull*

Chapter 38

Behemoth	*Something huge or enormous*

Chapter 39

Razzmatazz	*Showbiz glamour*
Silver-tongued-fox	*A charmer / charming*

Chapter 40

Cookie-duster	*Moustache*
Set of clubs	*Hands*
Anozer *(French accent)*	*Another*

Chapter 41

Zat *(French accent)*	*That*
Wizout *(French accent)*	*Without*
Ze *(French/German accent)*	*The*
Sink / Sinking *(French accent)*	*Think / Thinking*
Zis *(French accent)*	*This*
Voila	*French for: That is it / so there - an expression of finality*
Très bien	*French for: Very good*
BARNET	*THE finest word in the English language. Its origin is hair related. i.e. Nice barnet = Good haircut*
Time to sugar coat a response	*Say something in a nice way*
Elevenses	*Mid-morning tea break, usually around 11am*
Dunked	*Dipped*
High brow	*Intelligent*
Not on your Nellie	*Not on your life / Not likely / No chance - (you get the idea)*

Chapter 42

Batter	*Beat*

Chapter 43

Chit-chat	*Conversation or small talk*
Culinary sensation	*Hot dog / tasty food*

Space has been left on this page to allow for future updates.

If you have found that while reading this book there was a word or phrase that you didn't understand, then why not let us know.

In the second print run we will update The Rexasaurus accordingly, for the benefit of everyone's enjoyment.

Email the problem word or phrase to:

Rexasaurus@rexroman.com

Place in your subject header: REXASAURUS UPDATE

Sorry, but there will be NO reply to the email.

Please Note:
DO NOT SEND ANY attachments, pictures, CVs/resumes, offers of medical enhancement, tales of financial windfalls, etc, etc.

Anything other than a normal text email, containing genuine additions for the next print run, will be shredded by a spam filter and one of Roy's henchmen will be paying you a visit.

Genuine First Edition Copy

This book is number

- 596 -

of 1000

Chapters in the Life of
REX ROMAN

Episode 1

Chapter 1 – A Seaside Café in Cannes, France

June 2005

The sun shines on Cannes far more often and for far longer than it does on London, England. Designer shops, chic ladies and expensive cars are all in abundance, whilst the palm trees and golden sands only add to the feel good aura of the place.

Every April and October, there is a huge trade fair in Cannes attended by the great and the good from the exciting world of television. No top celebrities or self-respecting actors go there; these events are for the programme makers, buyers and sellers. It is no accident that many of us see the same TV show formats appearing around the world, merely changed to a localised language. These trade fairs are where the global domination of a television show is planned, bought and sold.

A positive benefit for all those attendees is that a trip to the picturesque French Riviera, on the company expense account, creates a fabulous opportunity to stay up all night drinking heavily while talking to members of the opposite sex.

The downside is that from 10am to 6pm many of these often hung-over movers and shakers are required to get together to do business. They seek to justify their jolly jaunt, mainly to the company accounts department, by holding mind-numbingly dull meetings about new programme content. These meetings often discuss the latest exciting reality TV formats, made only to 'enrich' our empty lives, and they are held in the basement of a concrete bunker of a building called The Palais. (*Aka the 'Palais des Festivals et des Congrès', to give The Palais its correct lengthy French title.)*

This is the same building that hosts the annual Cannes film festival, an event that is a magnet for movie stars. All the razzmatazz on the red carpet and the stairs outside, makes Cannes famous the world over. Dominating the seafront, The Palais sits between the grandeur of the large boats in the marina and a one mile stretch of beautiful sandy beach.

Running parallel with this enticing beach is a wide promenade where you can stroll, walk the dog or simply sit and admire the view of the calm Mediterranean Sea stretching out to the horizon. Next to the promenade is a road, which many of the locals use to cruise up and down in their open top vehicles or whizz along on their scooters. On the other side of the road is La Croisette. This is the main street in Cannes and home to some very impressive hotels, restaurants, numerous cafés and shops for the well-heeled.

With its clear view out across the bay, Levoilier is one of the better appointed cafés on La Croisette. Relaxing there at a table on the terrace, reading a copy of a freshly purchased English newspaper, is Rex Roman.

Rex is a British actor who now lives in Los Angeles, as he has done since 1980. Although Rex is 52-years-old, he has never married or been blessed with any children and as a result, is somewhat of a free spirit. If he decides to spend a few months 'resting' in France, then he doesn't have to worry that the movie industry will grind to a halt in his absence. Rex is in the sadder, more anonymous years of his acting career.

German film director, Frederick Hunzelbergerstraum, has lent Rex his two-bedroom Cannes apartment for as long as he wants it. They have remained friends since Frederick first introduced him to the art of film making in 1979, and barely 12 months ago, they worked together on an unsuccessful cinematic release.

Rex has a particular soft spot for France. With it being the destination of his first trip abroad, in 1975, it holds a special place in his heart.

'And for you, Monsieur?'

A waiter attentively appeared at the table as Rex raised his head from the paper, its pages filled with all the usual doom and gloom of life back in the UK.

'Un café-crème, s'il vous plaît.'

'Oui Monsieur,' replied the waiter, before scurrying away.

"HOUSE PRICES TO FALL 20%"

screamed the dramatic headline of the Daily Mail newspaper. Rex does love a Daily Wail and is kind of interested in such hysteria at first, although on closer inspection not entirely bothered for three simple reasons:

1. He read the headline: "HOUSE PRICES TO RISE 30%" the week before.
2. He has no intention of returning to England - EVER!
3. See 1 & 2, they're good enough.

Although England is the country of his birth, Rex now feels strangely disconnected from this green and pleasant land. A younger sister, a remarried father and a mother, with whom he shares a dysfunctional relationship, are the only family ties that he has there.

Top Rex Tip: *If you want to see more of your family, then why not move somewhere they like to go on holiday. Before long, they will be all over you like a cheap suit for the free accommodation. It works a treat. Rex sees his sister at least once a year thanks to the warm Californian climate.*

'Un café-crème, Monsieur.'

The waiter returned with a small cup of coffee, a separate metal pot of hot steamed milk, a bowl of individually wrapped sugar lumps and, of course, the complimentary biscuit. It may only be a fairly bland caramel biscuit, but it always seems to make the experience of a simple coffee that much more European, and hey - it's a *free* biscuit. Fantastic! Vive la France!!!

'Excusé moi, Monsieur...are you zat British actor, Rex Roman?' came the unexpected question as the pots were diligently arranged on the table.

'Well yes, yes I am as it happens,' replied Rex, slightly startled that a complete stranger knew his name.

'Oh Monsieur, I saw your last film.'

What's this? Someone in France had seen a film starring Rex? It must have been the 2004 release of the killer-thriller action movie - *Hunt Must Die.* This was good news. So good, that Rex removed his sunglasses to further engage his new fan.

'You did???...did you enjoy it?' asked Rex, hopefully.

'Nooooooooo...it was awful...a real stinker!' came the devastating critique.

For a moment there, Rex had ridden high on the crest of a wave. Another less than favourable appraisal of his work had quickly smashed him into the beach in a spectacular wipe out that left him feeling deflated. The waiter wasn't being mean spirited, just honest and brutally honest at that.

Hunt Must Die wasn't an awful film, confused perhaps but not awful. Rex had been woefully cast as a hitman who seemed to have no name; such was his mystique. His contract was to eliminate a man called Axel Hunt, played by the real star of the movie, the famous Hollywood legend - Mr X. *(The actor playing the unfortunate Mr Hunt threatened to sue us if we dared to mention his name.)*

The Hollywood leg end Mr X *(Who then said if the lawsuit failed, he would bury our cold lifeless bodies in the Las Vegas desert where no one would ever find us)* completely outshone Rex. In the end, the filmshoot turned into an acting masterclass led by this brilliant yet bad-tempered, paranoid teacher.

Thinking about it a little harder, Rex knew that the waiter was absolutely right…it was a stinker!

Rex was genuinely amazed that he had even been offered the role in the first place. It was well-known that he was a last resort choice for the job. Maybe the other preferred actors had taken the time to read the dire script and wisely declined. Rex hadn't, and he gladly accepted the offer.

Despite the hype, Hunt didn't die. His gory end was planned in the sequel - *Hunt Must Die…Again*!

However, poor reviews and terrible box office receipts for the first film seemed to suggest a very limited appetite for a second outing. Maybe a few people would be prepared to sit through yet another dreadful story line, only to see the grumpy Mr Hunt finally pop his clogs, but not enough of them to justify the expense of making it happen. Some bean counter at the studio had cancelled the sequel and robbed Rex of a valid excuse to swan around on location, pretending that acting was a proper job.

Fortunately the director and the writer were singled out for most of the criticism, but Rex was reviewed as: "Hopelessly out of his depth, he should stick to television".

Rex took some comfort from this harsh comment, as someone had actually noticed that he did appear on television from time to time. It was his occasional supporting role as the charming Dr. Michael Blake, in the 'one to miss' daytime TV show *Doctor Danger,* that had managed to sustain Rex as an actor for a number of years. This role afforded him a lifestyle of relative anonymity, with the added benefit of a small but steady income.

The real star of the show, and the character who received all the plaudits, was Dr. Steve Danger. This was a man who could solve any crime, always with a beaming smile and a cheeky wink, within the industry standard 42 minutes. The remaining 18 minutes of the one hour daytime slot were often filled with advertisements for superior life-enhancing products. Promises from 'no win/no fee' lawyers, for medical compensation claims, also added an ironic twist to every advert break in the show.

The latest season of *Doctor Danger* was all done. The makers had decided that the April market in Cannes was the perfect place to sell the show to overseas buyers. Rex had been offered an economy plane ticket, mainly as Maria in sales was off on maternity leave, and all he had to do in return was tell a few of his witty stories at a corporate dinner. With his film career in tatters, Rex had a period of six months with absolutely no work planned - so the trip was a must!

Now that the trade fair was over, rather than panic about his lack of employment, Rex had decided that this free time gave him a chance to savour life. France was as good a place as any to fill some lazy days due to his empty schedule.

'Aah, I always want to be an actor myself,' sighed the waiter, gazing at the clear blue sky, romantically considering life as a celebrity.

This is it, the moment every actor dreads. First you receive a poor review of your talents, swiftly followed by a reason why the reviewer will succeed where you have so clearly failed.

'I want to move to Ollywood and...aah...and be a big star.'

Rex rolled his eyes to the heavens. It was bad enough being told his movies stank, but now the ambitious critic was also intent on moving to Hollywood, to no doubt conquer Tinsel Town. Fresh off the plane, he would soon be cast as the dashing young Frenchman, Dr. Jacques, in the next revitalised series of *Doctor Danger,* replacing the ageing Dr. Michael Blake *(Rex)*.

Rex sat up straight and put his newspaper down on the wooden table, having decided that the waiter's dreams were as valid as any of his own. He didn't want to explain the true difficulties of following such a precarious career path, but a bit of small talk wouldn't hurt...

'So, what's your name?'

'My name? My name is Heffel...Heffel Sargoo...someday I will be famous, Monsieur.'

The irritating ring of a cell phone interrupted the conversation. Heffel was disappointed at this development as he was just finding his stride in some shameless self-promotion. He hadn't even shown Rex his French mime act, the one where the mime gets trapped in a box, so Heffel stood and waited for his chance.

Staring at the phone's display, Rex knew exactly who it was...

'Mr Handsome, how are you?'

'I'm fine thanks, Rex. My dear boy, where are you?'

'I'm sitting outside a café in Cannes, currently receiving a bad review from a waiter.'

'Are you still there? That's been two months!'

'I'm taking it easy,' said Rex, feebly trying to justify his laziness.

'Taking it easy? From what exactly? Anyway, look, I've heard something that may interest you. Hear me out, I want you to think carefully about this...'

Crispin Hansen is one of Rex's dearest friends. Their history dates back to 1976, and Rex regards Crispin as a loyal friend. He is not one of the fair-weathered variety - that were seemingly in abundance during the glory years but quick to leave as the predicted fame and fortune failed to materialise - he is solid and reliable.

Officially, Crispin acts as Rex's theatrical agent in the UK, yet when Rex left Britain in 1980, vowing never to return, some people suggested that this transatlantic separation would end their friendship. They were wrong. Despite the distance, the two have remained in contact throughout the years with unwavering regularity.

Rex insists on calling Mr Hansen by the far more interesting title of *"Mr Handsome"*- mainly as he thinks it's hilarious. In fact, the names that Rex affectionately associates with his mentor and long-time friend are:

1. Handsome *("Mr" is optional, depending on the mood)*
2. Sir *(Rock solid respect)*
3. CH *(Crispin's initials)*

Now that his friend was on the phone, Rex was wondering if *Doctor Danger* had been cancelled and he'd finally been found out for the fraud that he was. He could not possibly have imagined the shocking news he was about to hear...

'Pink Floyd are reforming! They're playing at a one-off charity gig in London, a few weeks from now. It's the classic line-up back together again. First time in 25 years. They're back, Rex.'

Boom! That was it, a bombshell of a statement.

'Holy Moly!' exclaimed Rex; a bizarre expression but definitely one of his favourites. 'When are they playing in the States?'

'They're not. This is it, my boy. A one shot deal. It's going to be a huge concert with loads of big names performing. It's all about highlighting the problems of Third World debt and poverty, so everyone's getting behind it. You remember that *Live Aid* gig, it's that sort of idea again. Anyway, I know you always were a massive Pink Floyd fan, so I had to tell you the news. Hot off the press this one.'

'Crikey!...I'm stunned...thanks for the tip, Handsome. How come you always get to hear about this stuff?'

'Contacts, Rex. Contacts. So, can I tempt you into coming back to London to see this gig? I know you've got issues, but that was a long time ago now. Besides, you can't let past sadness block your future happiness, it's just not right. It's time to move on from this whole London phobia thing.'

'But I still miss…oh, you know what happened…it's crazy, I know it is. It's just that…well, it's been so long, so much water has gone under the bridge.'

'That was all a lifetime ago, my boy.'

'I know, I know. I'm just scared that if I come back then I'll get too stuck in the past. Even now, I still wonder what might have been.'

'Oh Rex,' sighed Crispin.

'I'm happy now, Handsome. I finally know who I am, and I like it that way. My life feels settled these days.'

Crispin was a witness to the full story of why Rex was in such turmoil when he left England. He had accompanied his client to Heathrow airport, wishing him luck and happiness when he bid him farewell some twenty-five years prior. Crispin also knew how incredibly important the band, Pink Floyd, had been to Rex as a young man in the Seventies. It often felt like their music was a backdrop to Rex's very existence and influential in so many key chapters of his life. The news that the band were now reforming was an unexpected bolt from the blue, which was going to take some time to digest.

'Look Rex, I know some people. If I make a substantial donation to this worthy cause, then I can get both of us into the Golden Circle near the front. We'll have full backstage area privileges...which, as you well know...means decent food, bearable toilets and somewhere comfortable for me to rest my weary bones from time to time...what do you think?'

Crispin Hansen was a successful agent because he was a superb salesman, and he had just made a sales pitch of the highest order. He was applying a lesson in hype which was sending Rex's otherwise perfect day into a freefall of indecision. Rex started thinking…

'Pink Floyd back together? It's like all of your dreams coming true at once. They said it would never happen, and here it is. Finally! Why London? Why not New York? Why not Los Angeles? Why not anywhere else but London?

Then again, why not London? They are a British band after all. Worldwide media coverage from one of the greatest capital cities there is. The G8 summit is being held in Britain next month. It has to be London. Oh crap!

This needs to be considered, really seriously considered.'

'Can I think about this for a while, Mr Handsome?'

'Of course, but try not to think about it for too long. These tickets will be like gold dust, so I need to confirm I want them today. I'm telling you, this show will be a big deal. Everyone and their dog will want to go.'

'When is it exactly?' Rex enquired.

'Saturday the Second of July, open air in Hyde Park.'

Crispin could sense that Rex was warming to the idea. Previously, all requests for any return to London, or indeed anywhere in the UK, had long been dismissed by this point in the conversation. This band was the only weakness that Rex had, and Crispin knew it.

'Let me have a think about this one. I'll call you back later, I promise.'

'Okay, my boy. But don't over complicate things as usual. Just say yes and we'll sort out all the flight stuff some other time. Tell you what…I'll even foot the bill as a special treat. I'd be so happy to see you back here on home soil again.'

'That's very generous, Mr Handsome. I will definitely call you later.'

Damn, Crispin was good. He had just made the whole travel issue disappear as if by magic, and then, with another master stroke, had pitched in the "home soil again" comment. This nostalgic seed was designed to grow inside a heart that had been secretly homesick for a long time.

Rex placed his mobile phone back on the table and poured the steamed milk into his coffee, adding a lump of sugar to sweeten. Heffel had moved away to serve other tables, having abandoned his mime act for the time being.

As Rex stirred his drink, so his mind began to wander. He slumped back into a chair with a coffee in his hand, while the glorious sunshine and calm blue sea conspired to create a seemingly perfect setting. This was the ideal place for a man to spend some time reflecting on his memories.

Why couldn't Rex return to the country of his birth? What was the big deal anyway? What was his problem? Rex needed to make a careful examination of the past so that he could make an informed decision about his future. He had the time on his hands to start at the beginning…

Chapter 2 – Meet Paul

12th August 1952 - 6th March 1967

Paul David Charles Woozley was born on the 12th of August 1952, in a run-down part of North London, not too far from Hackney marshes. The marshes are an open green-grass area perfect for playing football, and it was on these fields that Paul enjoyed many Sunday morning matches throughout his childhood.

A mentally unstable mother and an often angry father meant the atmosphere in the family home was usually tense. Thankfully, adoring grandparents took care of Paul on most weekends. This situation provided him with an opportunity to play various classic board games with his grandfather while enjoying a house free of conflict.

Marie and Bill, the paternal grandparents, were simply the most wonderful people in Paul's life. They expressed their love and adoration for Paul on a daily basis, supporting him no matter what he wanted to do. He was their first grandchild, and that was always a distinct advantage.

On the 17th of September 1957, following months of furious parental rows, Paul's father left the family home for good. Paul was distraught to see his much-loved father leave, chased down the street by his hysterical mother, as the neighbours enjoyed the show. New, unfamiliar emotions of fear and insecurity made Paul worry about what would become of him. Being just 5-years-old, he failed to understand the rejection he felt and the low self-esteem this event would trigger in later life. He would only appreciate the situation, and his father's reasons for leaving, as he became older, and it all became clearer looking back.

From here on, money was tight. Lots of the other kids at school made fun of Paul purely because he received free dinners, courtesy of the state. His mother, Sandra, was not well-known for her economical skills, and it was easy to predict that some form of crisis would always be just around the corner. The days regularly began with the sound of her screaming and bursting into tears when the postman delivered yet another daily reminder of some overdue bill. Sandra's life was one of constant financial mayhem.

A younger sister, Anna, completed the family unit at home. The warring siblings often fought in private, managing to keep an unconvincing truce in front of others. Anna was an overweight child while Paul was stick-thin and quite tall for his age. With their birthdays just 13 months apart, they would attend the same primary and junior schools, where many of the other children cruelly labelled them 'fatty and skinny', on account of their differing body shapes. This often bothered Paul, making him self-conscious about his lack of weight and perceived weakness.

Not too long after Paul's father left home, his mother married an alcoholic, ex-con named Ray, against the concerned advice of everyone around her. Even Ray's mum warned Sandra not to do it, but she wouldn't listen. Any chance of happiness at home was promptly cancelled for the next 12 years.

To avoid his depressing home life, Paul could often be found wandering in Highbury Fields; a small local park tucked away behind Highbury Corner. This was somewhere to play football or cricket, depending on the season, with other kids from the neighbourhood. In fact, Paul would search for any outside activity he could find, just to escape the daily misery of 102 Roman Way.

In 1963, aged 11, Paul began his first year at his new senior school, Winston Comprehensive. Here he would spend the next five years furthering his education in preparation for eventual employment. Hopefully Paul could achieve some good exam grades and subsequently get a well-paid job to help ease his mother's monetary woes. However, the prospect of working hard for a living was a daunting one, so all manner of fanciful ideas and diverse interests were being added to a makeshift career list.

Much to Paul's relief, Anna had decided to go to a different senior school. Finally the 'fatty and skinny' jokes might just stop, well during school hours at least.

Overall, school was a happy place, somewhere safe. Definitely the best memories of Paul's childhood were school related. A place of friends and a place of freedom compared to the prison camp atmosphere at home, imposed by chief warden Ray Parker and his mutt of a German Shepherd dog - Rex.

Winston was a fairly large mixed school run by the seemingly austere headmaster, Mr Joe Graham. About 1500 pupils were divided into five separate years, each containing approximately 300 students. Year 1 was for the fresh-faced 11-12-year-olds, Year 2 for those aged 12-13 and so on... until you were an old-timer in Year 5, but at least you were top of the social pile.

Mr Graham was scarily assisted by his younger deputy, a Count Dracula look-alike named Mr Brian Goff. To be sent to see this Lord of the Vampires was easily the most terrifying experience any student could suffer.

It was during morning assembly on the 6th of March 1967, with Paul now aged 14, that the headmaster announced the imminent arrival of a new boy. Everyone was instructed to make an extra special effort to help him settle in.

'Why? What's so special about a new boy?' seemed to be the indignant ripple of unspoken thought running around the large wooden hall. The 300 or so students of Year 4, shivering on the cold floor, didn't seem that supportive.

'His name is Bradley Milwee, and he is joining us from America,' continued Mr Graham, projecting his voice across the room from his podium position on the stage.

'Bradley Wee Wee! He sounds a bit wet, or maybe he's French?' uttered some unfortunate, far too close to the bat-like hearing of Mr Goff.

There was a modicum of chuckling, a few guffaws but mostly tittering at this poor harmless joke. It seemed that Mrs Billicombe, the geography teacher, had a crafty snigger, but she stifled it well. The titters didn't last long as Goff stood up and echo located his prey.

'Banks, my office now!' shouted the enraged Count Dracula look-alike; veins' throbbing in his neck, sensing it was time to eat.

A deathly silence fell over the hall and 299 or so pairs of eyes focussed on the now terrified Clive Banks, as he slowly rose to his feet. Clive was not a bad lad, just a bit of a joker that's all. His impulsive comic one-liner was not particularly well-timed, and he was about to be ominously frogmarched off to Goff's lair, probably for a severe talking to at best. At worst, it was definitely the cane. Goff was an expert with the cane. Three good whacks across the buttocks and you were sitting on extra cushions for a week.

This dramatic event would be the hot topic of discussion at morning break, that was for sure.

Instant justice always was a good correctional method at Winston. If you stayed in line, you never had any problems. You quickly learned who to fear, and Mr Goff should definitely be Number One on your list. Mr Linden was secure in his position at Number Two, and new, in like a rocket, storming to Number Three was - Mr Stiles.

The formerly placid art teacher, Ken Stiles, had grown increasingly angry in the last six months. The irritation of so many students taunting him with the words: 'Oi…Nobby!' was becoming apparent. Naturally this was usually behind his back as he walked across the playground, so it was difficult for him to accurately pinpoint the culprits.

The offending remark was of course a reference to the toothless England football legend, Nobby Stiles, who had become a national hero of the time. Only the year before, in July 1966, England had won the Football World Cup, and the whole country went bananas in celebration.

'So, as I was saying, I want you to welcome young Bradley to our school,' continued Mr Graham, once the doors at the end of the hall had closed, indicating the exit of Banks and the Prince of Blood.

Most of the students were still in deep shock at this forced departure, but they managed to sufficiently recover to hear the word 'Dismissed' as the headmaster stepped down from his perch. This most cherished of school words meant that they could now leave behind the cold floor of the assembly hall and go back to the relative warmth of the classrooms.

Returning from assembly, Paul saw that Mr Stephenson and Mrs Billicombe were in the same tutor room. They were chatting and laughing about Banks while sharing a coffee. That coffee smell, fresh from a flask, was a wonderful aroma and filled the room nicely. As they had adjacent tutor rooms, Paul always saw lots of his two favourite teachers.

Ray Parker had attended Winston some 17 years prior and was a rotten egg even then. He always was trouble, and he no doubt always would be. Graham Stephenson had been at the school long enough to remember Ray as a boy, and he intensely disliked the troublesome student. The teacher took pity on Paul. He had a pretty good idea what was probably going on at home, yet this was not a subject easily discussed.

Paul had noticed that his class started to divide into two camps at lunchtimes. There were the sporty types, who went out onto the school field or tarmac yard to either play football or netball (or both!). Then there were those who headed straight for the drama block or music room. These were the arty types and a much smaller group. The girls went there for the drama (they love a bit of drama); the boys went there for the girls! Paul was a moth drawn to the creative flame, and he would choose the arts, over sports, any day of the week. Besides, with him being so thin he really felt the cold weather, and the drama block was always warm. Winters in England were cold back in 1967, really cold compared to the mild winters and sun-drenched summers enjoyed in paradise Britain nowadays.

Lunchtimes were the favourite part of Paul's day and usually spent either messing about with various musical instruments or inventing characters for school plays. Miss Winterbottom was the head of drama and incredibly popular. She had an unfortunate surname that caused much mirth amongst the students of Winston, but she could take the joke. Her voice was unique too, as she came from somewhere called Newcastle.

Not many of the students knew where this exotic sounding overseas destination was until Mrs Billicombe pointed out one day, to the enlightened few, that it was actually a city in the North East of England.

Gathering with friends during lunch was an escape for Paul. Making music, acting, painting, writing and anything artistic appealed to him. It was creative; it was fun. Such escapism obviously planted a seed in his mind, and that seed would later grow into something much, much bigger…

Chapter 3 – New Kid In Town

Tuesday 7th March 1967

On arrival at Winston, Paul thought it seemed a day much like any other on the 7th of March 1967. By the end of it, things would never be the same again.

Paul's school day began at 8.50am with a twenty minute tutor period. He was sat in class, aimlessly doodling on some scrap paper, while Mrs Billicombe took the register and informed the thirty students of class 4b about the latest school events.

Hilary Billicombe had been involved in a serious car accident some years earlier. Consequently, she had completely lost her sense of smell. The teenage boy's dream weapon of a stink bomb was an absolute waste of ammunition on Hilary, and besides, why target the good teachers when there were so many others far more deserving?

Just after 9am, Mr Graham knocked on the classroom door. Everyone stood to attention behind their desks, in total silence, as he entered the room. With him, was a gangly-looking kid with shoulder length hair, a big smile and a healthy suntan. It soon became apparent, to most of the girls in class, that he was much more attractive than many of the other boys in school. He sparked their interest and set a few hearts fluttering.

'Good morning, 4b.'

'Good morning, sir,' the class chanted in unison.

'Please be seated,' instructed Mr Graham. Everyone swiftly followed the principal's request until only he, Mrs Billicombe and the new kid remained standing in front of the class.

'Class 4b, this young man is Bradley Milwee. He is new to this school and indeed new to this country as he is joining us all the way from California, in the United States of America.'

Everyone gawped at Bradley, which seemed to make him look a little uncomfortable.

'I want you to make him feel welcome and help him adjust to life in this school,' continued the headmaster.

Bradley made a weak attempt at waving hello to the staring boys and giggling girls, only to look totally relieved when he was escorted to a desk by the door and asked to sit down next to Tim Bell.

Tim was a short, rotund lad with a great sense of humour. He was also a prefect, which meant he was trusted by the teachers, so he had been assigned the task of taking care of the new boy. Bradley would be okay with Tim as his first new friend in class.

* * *

A loud bell heralded lunchtime at 12.30pm and the start of a one hour break. Paul strolled into the dining area, which was actually the assembly hall, only now with added tables and chairs. Hatches on one of the side walls had been opened to expose the kitchens where the daily banquets were prepared. Pink blancmange, custard with skin, lumpy semolina with jam, stew with extra gristle and hairy mash - all of these treats were five star fayre compared to the food Paul was served at home, so he eagerly wondered what was on offer today.

Each dining table could seat eight people. On Paul's table, Banks was recounting the horrors of the day before and his experience in Goff's office. A dramatic reconstruction, with full sound effects, that made the diners gasp in-between mouthfuls.

Having gathered the gossip from The Bankster, Paul headed straight for the drama block as soon as he'd cleared away his plate. Today's particular feast was three fish fingers and chips, swiftly followed by jam sponge drowning in custard, all of which was now sitting warmly in Paul's stomach.

The drama block and the music room were all contained in the performing arts department at Winston. Walking through some large swinging doors and into the reception area of this home for the creative spirit, Paul could hear someone playing guitar.

'Crikey!' he thought. *'Whoever's playing that is good, really good.'* As Paul moved closer towards the sound, he wondered who this mystery star could be. When he entered the music room, he was surprised to see the new American boy sitting on a desk.

Bradley had an acoustic guitar in his hands, and several girls were sat in chairs, dreamily staring at this new kid in town. He'd only been at Winston for just over three hours, yet he was already a firmly established heart-throb. With an outsider now the centre of attention, the power of music made a real impression on Paul as he watched the girls swoon.

As the daily drama club was about to start, Paul couldn't stay to watch the entire impromptu gig, even though he was highly appreciative of the performer's talents. He left Bradley wooing the girls with his Californian charm and taking requests for any Beatles song his fan club cared to choose.

The Lothario swine!

Twenty minutes later in the drama block, a noisy scenario was being played out. Paul was the referee in a fictitious boxing contest between two gladiators of the ring, and the atmosphere was electric. No punches were physically being thrown, this was the acting part of the class, but the audience of fellow students still hoped for a mishap. Bradley entered the room and sat on a chair by the door, surrounded by his female admirers.

'Alreet noo, that'll dee far the day,' shouted the delightfully fragrant Miss Winterbottom in her wonderful Geordie dialect. She accompanied her instruction with loud hand-clapping, to reinforce her command that playtime was now over.

Despite a few moans and groans the crowd began to disperse, and as Paul reached the exit, Bradley spoke to him for the first time...

'That looked fun, man.'

'Yes, it is. I love it,' replied Paul, secretly in awe of the new kid and his entourage.

'Yeah, it was cool. Wanna walk with me?'

Bradley stood up, and the pair began their slow return to class for post-lunchtime registration.

'You're Bradley Milwee, aren't you?' asked Paul, already knowing the answer.

'Not when I play guitar I'm not,' replied Bradley in the best accent Paul had ever heard.

'Why? Who are you?' Paul was really perplexed by the last statement, regardless of how good it sounded.

'Bradley Mills.'

Paul went from perplexed to full-on confused.

'Look, Milwee is an awful name,' explained Bradley as the pair continued their snail-pace walk. 'But Bradley Mills sounds cool, so when I leave school, I'm gonna be known as Bradley Mills.'

'How can you?' asked Paul, struggling to understand.

'Simple. I just call myself Bradley Mills.'

'What just like that?'

'Yep. Just like that.'

Paul thought about this briefly before speaking...

'I hate my name, too,' he confessed, having long held this conclusion but only now having the courage to admit the truth. It felt good though, to finally get it out in the open.

'Well change it then,' said Bradley in a casual tone, unfazed by the bold confession.

'What to?'

There was a question that had no obvious answer. Paul had hated his name for years. No one could pronounce it, let alone spell it. His mother had remarried. His sister would surely marry someday, so eventually he would be the only one stuck with it.

Every time it was the same old story…

'Woozley…that's Wooz...ley…yes, I'll spell it for you,

W…O…O…Z…not an S…a Z…yes a Z…L…E...Y.'

Sigh!

'I've got an idea,' said Bradley, becoming a lot more animated and stopping in his tracks. 'What's the name of your first pet? You know, dog or cat, a real pet. Goldfish don't count.'

Paul didn't have to think about this for too long. It was prison warden Ray's patrol dog.

'Rex,' Paul replied.

'Yeah, I like that…man, that's killer.'

Bradley seemed to enjoy the answer.

'Now, what's the name of the street you live in?' was Bradley's follow-up question, his face indicating that he was really excited by this game.

'Roman Way,' said Paul. 'I live at 102 Roman Way.'

Bradley roared with laughter.

'That's it, that is it! REX ROMAN. Oh dude, that's the coolest name I have **ever** heard.'

'Is it? I don't get it.'

'Look, Rex is the name of your first pet; Roman is the first part of your home address,' explained Bradley. 'So when we add them both together, you have a new name that's good to go.'

The bell rang, signalling the official end of lunchtime, so the new friends quickened their pace back to class.

He didn't know it, but Bradley had just opened an escape hatch for Paul. An identity problem had been offered a solution, and this was now firing Paul's vivid imagination. It was clear to him that through this hatch lay a whole new life and a break from the past.

Now all Paul had to do, was jump…

Chapter 4 – Goodbye Paul…Hello Rex

Tuesday 7th March 1967

3.50pm was marked by three consecutive bell rings at Winston school. It was the most important time of the day for a majority of the students, as it signalled the end of lessons and the start of a stampede towards the school gates.

At 3.52pm Paul was not walking anywhere in a hurry. He was on a go slow, trying to think of something to do other than go home.

'Hey Rex,' a voice called from behind. 'Wait up!'

Paul knew it was Bradley because no one else at school spoke with an American accent. The deciding factor though, was that no one else called him Rex.

'Wanna hang out?' asked Bradley as he moved alongside with a big toothy grin on his face. The boy certainly had a fine set of gnashers.

'You know I'm always gonna call you Rex from now on, right?' stated Bradley, his mind made up.

'Yes, I've been thinking about that all afternoon…I think I like it.'

'Like it? Are you crazy? You gotta love it, it's a gift. This is your destiny. **You are Rex Roman**. I don't even know what your old name was, and I don't even care.'

Bradley had really taken this to heart. His enthusiasm was infectious and only seemed to add weight to the crazy notion that everything was that simple.

From outside the gates, a woman sounded a horn and began waving frantically as she stood by the open door of her car.

'Bradley…Brad…ley,' she cried, trying to gain some attention.

'If we're gonna be friends, I'm only gonna call you Rex. That's it. Nothing else. Not now, not ever! Deal?' said Bradley, issuing an ultimatum and holding out his right-hand as he did so.

The boys were stationary inside the school grounds, locked in tough negotiation, with a lone female voice demanding recognition just a few feet away. Paul thought about the terms briefly before nodding his head and shaking hands on the agreement.

'Cool! Rex Roman it is,' said Bradley, closing the deal. 'Let's go to my house, we can play KerPlunk or something…Mom!'

Answering the calling, Bradley turned to the gates and dragged his renamed companion the short distance to the parked car.

'Mom, this is my new friend, Rex. Can he come home and stay for a couple of hours, please?'

Mrs Milwee was a very pretty mousey-blonde. Immaculately dressed in a paisley outfit, she looked every inch a fashionista of the times. She also looked fairly small standing next to the pair of tall teenage boys, waiting for her response.

'Hi Rex,' she said, in a gentle American accent. Her voice was calming, and Rex immediately felt comfortable in her presence, unlike the experience of spending time with his own mother. Turning to Bradley, she gave him a loving smile and took his school bag. 'Sure honey. That would be swell.'

Sold! Two deals in two minutes. Bradley had wrapped Mom around his finger and demonstrated his potential as a budding salesman. Mom could now complete some chores and leave the boys to entertain themselves. Rex had a valid reason not to return home for a few hours. Everyone was a winner.

Today was after all Bradley's first day at Winston, and a mutual admiration had made a quick progression to friendship. The more Rex heard his new name, the more he liked it, and he knew there was no turning back.

That was it. Goodbye Paul…Hello Rex.

If being renamed after a dog wasn't strange enough for one day, even more unusual adventures were laying in wait back at Bradley's house, for unbeknown to Rex, he would soon encounter the true phenomenon that is Bradley's father...

ROY MILWEE

Chapter 5 – Chez Milwee

Tuesday 7th March 1967

Arriving at chez Milwee, Rex was immediately impressed. The house was large, detached and obviously well-kept. It wasn't like the cramped, terraced, hovel of a home he lived in at 102 Roman Way.

To have a detached house in London was a big deal. Most of the outer parts of the city consisted of flats and poor social-housing. Away from the central attractions of Leicester Square and Piccadilly Circus, London could be a bit rough out in the boroughs. That was not the case in this street. Rex could tell this house had some class, even from inside the car.

'Okay, boys. We're home,' said Mrs Milwee, turning off the ignition and unclipping her seatbelt. 'You two go and play while I make you a snack. How about a PBJ?'

'Yeah!' replied Bradley, enthusiastically.

Once inside, Rex was instantly amazed how clean the hall was. Everything was tidy, meaning he could even see the walls and carpets. Nothing too remarkable about that. An everyday occurrence you might think, but then you've never been to 102 Roman Way. That place was a dump.

Old papers, magazines and Ray's enormous collection of Haynes car manuals littered every surface. Sandra's trademark was in the form of handwritten notes which were dotted all over the house. In her mind, if instructions weren't strewn everywhere she went, she wouldn't be able to complete her tasks.

The dog had shed a mountain of hair throughout the downstairs, leaving a hairy haze on the carpets, oh and he stank like you would not believe. Anna had chipped in a few discarded sweet wrappers, a lovely touch which was only rivalled by her toast crust collection. These food remnants were beautifully spread around various locations, presumably just in case she got a bit peckish, or, more than likely, she couldn't be bothered to return her plate to the kitchen after consuming her snack.

Last but not least, there was the 'pièce de résistance' - **clothes!** Everywhere in the house, jumpers, trousers, underwear and even towels fought running battles to get the last piece of free space. Some were dirty; some were clean. Only a sniff test could identify which, or maybe one of Sandra's notes held the answer. All of these factors played their part in making the house look and feel like a real dump.

The only tidy room was Rex's bedroom, which was spotless. Everything was in exactly the right place in an act of futile rebellion against the tyranny of chaos that reigned everywhere else. The neatly drawn 'No Dogs Allowed' poster on the door outside ensured at least one pleasantly fragrant room in this dismal dwelling, but behind that closed bedroom door, Rex would often feel lonely and unloved.

'Wanna play a game?' asked Bradley as he led the way into the lounge.

'Yes, great,' replied Rex, just happy to be in such pleasant surroundings.

'Do you know how to play Monopoly?' quizzed Bradley, hopeful of a positive response.

'Monopoly! I love Monopoly!' Rex enthused.

Monopoly is one of those timeless, classic board games that Rex had played on many occasions with his grandfather; it was their favourite game. Nan would make cups of tea and bake cakes in the kitchen while all manner of wheeling and dealing was taking place in the lounge.

Tea, Rex had discovered, was a fantastic vehicle for increasing the consumption rate of biscuits. The average person might take a custard cream, have a bite, crunch and munch away, follow with a sip of tea to wash down the flavour, and repeat. Not a bad technique, a tad amateur perhaps but not bad.

However, a professional like Rex would dunk his custard cream fully into the tea. This technique would soften the heavenly biscuit and therefore increase the rate at which the rest of the packet could be consumed. Sometimes he could eat three or four biscuits in the time it took his Grandad to eat one.

Bradley was an only child, so he was excited at having someone new in the house who would soon succumb to his gaming skills. Hurriedly, he assembled all of the pieces for the forthcoming Monopoly match on a large coffee table that dominated the lounge. The devoted mother suddenly returned with a tray, containing two plates of sandwiches and two glasses of milk.

'Here you go, boys,' she said, placing the tray on a sideboard next to the fireplace.

Rex couldn't believe it. What a kind lady. He barely knew her, but she had already made him a sandwich.

'Can we have a few chips please, Mom?' asked Bradley as he began counting out the appropriate sums of cash to start the game.

'Chips?' thought Rex.*'Why on earth would you have chips with a sandwich?'*

When Mrs Milwee returned with a bag of Golden Wonder crisps, Rex was relieved to have solved the mystery...

'Aah crisps,' he said, unable to contain the revelation. 'We call these crisps, Bradley. Chips are called crisps in England.'

Rex's fertile mind had another question: *'If chips are crisps, then what are proper chips called? The sort we get served at school on a daily basis.'*

'Right, I get it,' acknowledged Bradley. 'What you call chips, we call French fries.'

'French fries?' gasped Rex. 'Ooh, how cosmopolitan!'

The cultural exchange was in full flow. New words were being given new meanings and horizons broadened.

'Have you ever had a PBJ?' asked Bradley, realising this staple of the American diet could be a first for his new friend.

'I don't know,' replied Rex. 'What is it?'

'This is the taste sensation you have always dreamed of - Peanut Butter and Jelly.'

Bradley held half a sandwich in his hands like it was a piece of treasure. He took a bite right out of the middle and groaned in ecstasy.

Rex winced. Peanut butter was of course an acceptable treat, but jelly?

Jelly was served at school for dessert, usually accompanied by custard. Proving its versatility it could also be enjoyed with ice cream, tinned milk or perhaps even double cream, but in a sandwich? This was probably one use too far for Rex.

Bradley opened the crisp packet, shared out the contents between both plates and handed Rex his snack.

Rex separated the two bits of bread and peeked inside...

'Okay, that's definitely peanut butter on the bottom, ooh crunchy not smooth, my favourite. Now, what's this red stuff on the top slice? Hang on, that's not jelly…that's JAM!'

'Jam…jelly is jam!' blurted out Rex at the joy of his latest edible discovery.

'Oh right,' agreed Bradley, nonchalantly. He was busy eating. 'What you call jelly, we call Jell-O in the States.'

Rex hungrily took a bite of his snack. Suddenly, in an instant, he was a convert. This was a new taste sensation of the highest order. Throw in a few crisps, a glass of milk and this was going to be the finest meal ever.

'This is delicious,' said Rex, confirming the obvious.

'I thought you might like it,' replied Bradley, momentarily pausing between mouthfuls.

Feeling obliged to return the favour and enlighten his new friend with a great tip for life, Rex thought hard as he ate, before offering a real gem…

'Do you know how to play *Speed Monopoly*?'

'Speed Monopoly?' questioned Bradley, looking up from his feast, his eyes widening in expectation.

'Yes, my Grandad taught me. It's like the regular game but improved, faster and better.'

'Never heard of it. C'mon show me. We have to play,' said Bradley, excited by the prospect of learning a new twist on his favourite game.

Monopoly is a game of strategy, merciless rent collecting, property empires, jail avoidance and luck of the dice. It can also take a long time. Therefore, Grandad Bill had invented the lesser known but far superior version - *Speed Monopoly.*

In this variation only three notes are used - £50, £100 & £500. If a price is £12, it becomes rounded up to £50. If a price is £120, it becomes rounded down to an even £100. Sometimes you win; sometimes you lose. The real genius of these new rules means that even the normally well-avoided brown properties, just after 'Go', massively rise in status, far beyond their regular rental values in the normal version of the game. Downmarket, cheap to buy, but each stay in such an establishment is going to cost the grumbling tenant a minimum of 50 smackers.

The key to success is simple: ***Buy everything you can.***

Discounting Bradley's earlier effort, Rex took control of the bank and dealt the cash. Both players received 5 x £500, 5 x £100 and 5 x £50. All of the other notes were put away. When Bradley took the first roll of the dice, the excitement began to build. This was a welcome high to offset the low of finishing the best sandwiches that anyone could wish for.

Rex collected the empty plates and glasses, put them onto the tray and returned them to the kitchen while Bradley placed the Chance and Community Chest cards on the board.

'Thank you, Mrs Milwee. That was delicious,' said Rex, resting the tray next to the sink.

'You're welcome, thank you for bringing the plates out.'

'My Grandad told me I should always return my plate after I've eaten. He told me it was polite to do so.'

Bradley's Mum looked at Rex and smiled.

'Oh Rex, you can call me Kate.'

'Okay, Mrs Milwee,' Rex replied, completely avoiding the suggestion as he returned to the lounge.

Battle lines were drawn, yet Rex noticed that Bradley only had four £500 notes on his side of the table. He had definitely been given five. This could mean just one thing - Bradley was applying the old 'secret £500' trick.

This defensive masterstroke involved placing the missing note under the board nearest to where you sat. If the game didn't quite go according to plan, you could magically produce the missing note, in one crafty move, allowing the game to be extended just a little bit longer. Cunning, brilliant!

This was going to be an epic duel...

Chapter 6 – A Giant Named Roy

Tuesday 7th March 1967

'Damn Limeys!'

A deep angry voice bellowed from the hall, closely followed by the sound of a door slamming. Rex and Bradley looked up from their battlefield, startled by the noise.

Two hours had passed, and three games had been played, with Rex currently ahead 2-1. Bradley was making excuses that his reputation, as a ruthless trader in American hotels and power stations, was being compromised by a lack of knowledge about the English locations found in his British version of the game. He had thoroughly embraced the idea of *Speed Monopoly,* as it meant more games per hour. What had originally started out as a '*Best of Three* - Championship' had now been extended to a '*Best of Five* - World Series'.

'Honey, what's wrong?' asked a soothing voice, in relaxed response to the wild hurricane of rage blowing in the hall. As the brave Mrs Milwee rushed to the storm front, she saw her husband drenched from the waist down.

'Some jerk just splashed me driving by in his car, look at me Kate! Look at me!!!'

As the man of the house dripped on the carpet, flapping his arms like a giant penguin, Kate tried her absolute best to suppress a giggle. Waving a deflated umbrella in his right-hand, it had offered scant protection against the offending London motorist.

Rex and Bradley hadn't even noticed the rain that had been hammering down outside for the last ninety minutes. They were far too engrossed in their game.

'You go change, honey. I'll bring you a scotch and soda,' said the loving wife as she planted a kiss on her husband's cheek, offering her comfort and support during this crisis.

'Bradley has a new friend over,' she continued, pointing to the lounge.

One of those 'damn limeys' was currently sitting in the next room, trembling at the prospect of a giant coming through the door. He wasn't disappointed.

Roy Milwee was a giant. He must have been about 6-foot, 5-inches tall, and as wide as the doorway. (*For those people more used to metric measurements, that converts to one big son of a gun.*) Roy was possibly one of the biggest men that Rex had ever seen. A large moustache bristled on his top-lip, and thick, black hair completed an impressive profile.

'Hi Brad.'

'Hi Roy,' said Bradley in response to his father.

Rex's eyes popped out on stalks. He was astonished that Bradley had just called his father by his first name.

'Hello young man,' said the giant, staring at Rex.

'Hello sir.'

Good answer. There were three possible responses as Rex saw it: *"Hello Roy"*, *"Hello Mr Milwee"* or *"Hello sir"*.

The prospect of further igniting the volcanic temper that had arrived in the house, only a couple of minutes ago, had to be avoided. Rex stuck to rock solid respect with his response, to minimise the chances of any more eruptions. He *was* going to stand up, but seeing as he had been kneeling on the lounge floor, hunched over a coffee table for two hours, his legs had gone uncomfortably numb.

With Roy having left the room, his large muscular frame made an undignified squelching as he stomped up the stairs. Rex was sat in the lounge wondering if this was a good time to leave.

'What does your Dad do, Bradley?' asked Rex, expecting the answer to be: professional sportsman, astronaut or assassin.

'He's a troubleshooter or something like that,' replied Bradley, wondering who owned Old Kent Road and unsure if he had collected his 'Pass Go' money during the recent commotion.

Rex knew it...

'Of course he is! Roy's an assassin, not just any assassin but the best there is. Bradley has pretty much confirmed it. Anyone that big must specialise in murder. Roy sees trouble and makes the problem go away by shooting it, hence the term "troubleshooter"...

'Why is he here in London? Who is he here to kill? He must be on top secret undercover work for the U.S. government. Maybe I already know too much. I know where Roy lives and what he looks like, so now I have to be eliminated to stop me from talking. I won't talk - honest...oh, blimey!...I'd better get out of here.'

Rex had of course begun connecting **'The Chain of Doom'.**

Take a point, any point, and with accomplished ease Rex could then form a chain of pessimistic thoughts that would spiral into an apocalyptic ending. This Chain of Doom could be connected at lightning speed, anytime, anyplace, anywhere. All that was needed to set such dark drama in motion was a very vivid imagination.

'I think I should go now,' said Rex, feeling uncomfortable at the prospect of Roy returning any time soon.

'But we haven't finished the game,' whined Bradley.

'That's okay, I forfeit. That makes it two-two. We'll play again another day.'

This, for Bradley, was the ultimate result. A respectable draw meant that he could retain his unbeaten record. In the meantime, he could further hone his newly acquired *Speed Monopoly* skills by playing a game with his mother, who was no match for such a shrewd landlord.

'Okay,' agreed Bradley, knowing he was onto a good thing. 'I'll get Mom to take you home.'

* * *

While Roy had a soak in the bath, no doubt washing off the blood spatters from his day at work, Rex sat in the back of the car. He was thinking about the stack of homework he had to complete that evening.

'Where exactly do you live, Rex?' asked Kate, looking in the car's rear-view mirror and waiting for instructions.

Bradley was also sitting in the front and had told his mother to head towards Winston school, so she had already begun the journey back in that direction.

It was at this moment that Rex had a further panic attack. He couldn't face the idea of Bradley and his mother knowing the exact location of his wretched home address as he would be too embarrassed. They had a lovely, well-kept house in a decent street. Rex lived in the sort of area where Roy went to wipe out the scum.

'Oh, you can just drop me at the school, Mrs Milwee. Thanks.'

'Nonsense, Rex. It's raining, you'll get soaked.'

'No, no honestly, I live right near the school, and I've got an umbrella. I want to stretch my legs anyway. I've been sitting on the floor for hours.'

It sounded plausible enough. Apart from the fact that Rex didn't have an umbrella in his bag nor live that close to the school, the rest of it was pure gold.

'Okay hon, school it is.'

Back in his bedroom, having been drenched on the walk home, Rex changed into some dry clothes. Luckily he had made it back before Ray would stumble home in a drunken stupor, looking to start an argument.

Rex had declined the offer of any dinner for two reasons. Firstly, Sandra was an awful cook, and today's offering of liver and mash looked distinctly unappealing. Secondly, the PBJs had taken the edge off of his hunger rather well. A 9pm bowl of Frosties would be a tasty supper once the necessary homework tasks had been completed.

Rex took a sheet of paper and scribbled in big letters…

REX ROMAN

Staring at his handiwork and smiling, Rex stuck the paper to the wall, using some sticky tape on each corner to secure it. This hand written name certificate would be a constant daily reminder of his new persona.

Today had seen the start of a friendship, one that was going to lead to all manner of unbelievable adventures in the years to come…

Chapter 7 – The Slipper

May 1968

Gary Chivers was an idiot, a total idiot. Everybody at Winston school knew it. Today he was going to offer some undeniable proof of his own stupidity.

Rex and Bradley were minding their own business, talking nonsense, while they sat under a tree during school lunch break. They had been solid friends now for well over a year, and talking nonsense was one of their favourite pastimes. They often talked of pedalling around Europe on their bikes, sleeping in tents, living off the land and working jobs wherever they could find them. The naivety of youth was in full flow; it was fun to dream.

With final exams looming in just a few weeks, they were coming to the end of their time at Winston. The glorious May sunshine was beaming down on them, so the tree offered some welcome shade from the heat. It was a perfect day.

'Oi Yankee!'

The angry, intimidating bulk of Gary Chivers came storming across the field, closely followed by a group of underlings.

'Wot you bin sayin' to my girl?' he snorted, menacingly.

Rex and Bradley were taken aback by such hostility, quickly standing up to assess the danger. The school's most feared thug was bearing down on them at great speed, and he had a look in his eye that spelt trouble.

Other students on the school field sensed that something was about to happen, partly due to Gary's well-deserved reputation as a hothead, and began adding to the growing crowd gathered around the tree.

'Er…what girl?' replied Bradley as he came face-to-face with a hate-filled Gary.

'Julie Smiff. She's my girlfriend not yours, so keep yer filffy hands off!'

Gary certainly had a bee in his bonnet. He looked wild-eyed and was pointing his forefinger in a threatening manner. The situation felt tense.

'I haven't touched her,' protested Bradley. 'I don't really know who she is.'

This was true. Julie Smith was much more aware of Bradley than he was of her. In the same year, although not in the same class, she had heard Bradley playing his guitar and seen him around the school for the last fourteen months. She thought he was gorgeous and had made the mistake of vocalising such praise in front of her boyfriend.

Gary, with his Neanderthal leanings, had completely blocked out the minor detail that Bradley had never even knowingly spoken to Julie, and he was consumed by jealousy.

'Don't get clever wiv me, mate,' said Gary. The paradox of him calling Bradley a 'mate', as he prepared to launch an assault, was lost on Gary. All he could see was a threat.

'Look, buddy. I'm not...I really don't know what you're talking about.'

Bradley had his hands up, palms out, submissively trying to diffuse the situation.

The baying mob were in the mood for some midday brawling entertainment, so perhaps their interest was the catalyst for Gary feeling that he had to live up to his reputation. Without any further vocal warning, he punched Bradley straight in the stomach, in an uppercut movement. The shock of this blow winded Bradley, and he fell to the ground gasping for air.

The assembled crowd began to chant...

'Fight! Fight! Fight!'

Rex looked on, feeling sick. Here was his best friend, about to get pummelled by the school bully, and he felt totally and utterly helpless.

Bradley was in no position to fight back, but this wasn't enough for Gary. He was determined to make an example of his love rival, so he pinned him down on the grass by sitting on his chest and placing a knee on each shoulder. Gary was getting ready to go for the kill and eager to ruin those pretty-boy looks that Julie Smith found so appealing.

The thought of Bradley being beaten was too much for Rex, and he found his initial fear suddenly turn to rage. Without thinking of the consequences, he leapt at Gary with a flying tackle before any blows could be rained down on Bradley's face. He caught Gary mid-body, knocked him sideways and the pair lay in a heap, both stunned by the action.

It all happened so fast that Rex hadn't even started to connect the Chain of Doom. He had acted on instinct, raw instinct.

'BUNDLE!!!' screamed a voice from the crowd. As if things weren't bad enough already, now a crushing was imminent.

'Break it up!' bellowed another voice from above.

Rex looked up and was relieved to see Mr Stephenson. Having noticed the gathering on his lunchtime patrol duties, the teacher had arrived to break up the brawl and save the day. As he stood there with his hands on his hips, looking over the bodies on the ground, his face indicated that he was **not** amused.

'Right you three, my tutor room. Now!' came his angry instruction as he pointed back to the main building.

Slowly the boys all staggered to their feet, only to be escorted inside for a really good talking to - much to the frustration of the assembled fight fans.

* * *

Standing in a line, heads bowed, the trio silently awaited their punishment.

'I expect you've been up to your old tricks again then, Gary. I don't even want to hear your excuses. Go to Mr Goff's office and wait for me. Go!'

That was Gary dealt with, no chance to invent a story. Five years of being a notorious hooligan meant that he was a frequent visitor to Goff's lair. Rumour has it that Gary was used as a guinea pig; a spot of target practice for the sadistic deputy head. Gary had proven a useful tool in Goff's quest to perfect new and even more painful ways of inflicting the cane.

'I am so disappointed in you two,' said Mr Stephenson, looking directly at Bradley and Rex. They were stood behind a desk, hands clasped in front of them, both wearing hangdog expressions. 'What happened?'

'Gary came over and punched me for no reason,' explained Bradley, still in pain and close to tears.

'Yes, I can believe that. I really can,' confirmed the bespectacled English literature teacher as he nodded in agreement. 'And you Paul...what on earth were you doing?' He was obviously unaware that Paul was now called Rex.

'Bradley is my friend, sir. I just wanted to protect him,' faltered Rex, visibly upset by the whole incident.

At that moment, despite the requirement to punish all boys for fighting, the sympathetic teacher took pity on this noble action. Both boys had been set upon by the school bully and were simply sticking together to defend themselves. In reality, this was a display of loyalty that should actually be applauded; yet rules are rules.

'I understand. Well, in that case go and see Mr Linden after school to explain yourselves.'

Judgment was passed. Tom Linden was the undisputed Number Two on the 'teachers to be feared' list. His choice of punishment was the slipper, which would be a far more bearable whack on the rump rather than one delivered by the cane.

As luck would have it, Mr Linden was off on sick leave this week. All of the staff at Winston knew this.

'Get yourselves outside now, lads. Enjoy the rest of break.'

That was it, the pair were dismissed. With no immediate punishment and the bully taken care of, everything seemed normal again. Bradley and Rex returned to the playground while Mr Stephenson went off to ensure that Gary got a really good thrashing.

'Are you going to tell your Dad about this?' asked Rex as the pair went to find a bench to sit on.

'You betcha,' replied Bradley, confirming the worst.

'Well that's the end of Gary Chivers,' thought Rex. *'Once Big Roy tracks him down, he'll be in the Thames before he knows it wearing some concrete boots no doubt. Wonder if Roy will torture him first? Driving him around London in the boot of his car would be a good start and then…'*

The bell rang to indicate the end of lunchtime. An entirely unwelcome act of aggression had ruined an otherwise perfect day, but it had at least proved one thing for sure:

Bradley and Rex were the best of friends.

* * *

Back in Cannes, Rex was mentally connecting his thoughts again. A skill he had learnt in his youth, he was able to rapidly chain together key life events at lightning speed. Fortunately he had learnt to overcome the 'doom' part of the chain, so looking back was proving to be wonderful fun.

Heffel was loitering in the background, hoping to gain some attention, but Rex was still deep in thought, oblivious to the waiter's presence. Sipping his coffee, Rex was enjoying fond memories of his youth and of his school days in 1968. Having remembered the fight, now he would reflect on the flipside of that event…

Chapter 8 – Steve Brown

January 1970

Rex and Bradley had arrived at Islington Sports & Leisure Centre, pausing briefly before they entered. Not a particularly attractive looking place, they had come here to honour their pact in the house of pain. They had crossed the point of no return as they stepped through the front entrance that morning. They were both terrified.

'Two for Kung Fu, please,' gulped Rex, smiling nervously at the smartly dressed lady behind the reception desk. He presented her with a crisp £1 note that Roy had given him earlier with an approving nod.

'You don't pay here, love,' she replied, 'you pay the instructor in the class. You want to go and see Steve Brown. He's in the dance studio. Go through this door, up the stairs and then it's the first door on your left. Okay, love?'

Rex was puzzled. Had she heard him correctly? Why would you hold Kung Fu lessons in a dance studio? The Chain of Doom began to link in his mind… *'Wooden floors, no carpet, easier to mop up the blood and collect the teeth.'* Rex felt faint and sick with worry.

The pair left the reception area on the path towards their inevitable death by violent injury. There were lots of myths and rumours surrounding the martial arts. Bones could be broken in an instant. Bricks were pulverised into dust with bare hands. Grown men could be killed with a single touch. This is a dangerous pastime, but Bradley had decided that it all sounded exciting. What was he thinking?

Arriving at the dance studio, Rex noticed that there was a large clock hanging high on the wall outside. Underneath the clock was a notice board which advertised lots of other, safer activities available at the centre. An impressive looking white A4 size poster, with black writing and a few Chinese symbols, stood out…*(See note overleaf)*

Learn Kung Fu

Every Sunday 10am-12noon &
Thursday 7.30-9.30pm

The ultimate in self defence
control and discipline

Knowledge is power

Beginners class - 11am Sundays
(wear loose fitting clothes)

(**Note:** *The publishers have pointed out that due to budget cuts, they won't be recreating the true glory of this poster…tightwads!)*

Bradley had seen a similar poster on a previous visit to the sports centre when he had defeated his mother in a game of table tennis to win the 'Chocolate Chip Cookie' Cup Final. The poster was in a different location, but it contained the same exciting information. He had begged Rex to attend a beginners' class with him, so Rex had reluctantly agreed. The memory of the fight with Gary Chivers nearly two years ago still haunted Bradley. This was his way of allaying those fears.

It was 10.27am and the beginners' class started at eleven. *'Oh great, just my luck,'* thought Rex, *'thirty-three minutes to anticipate my untimely demise.'*

Shouts of savagery from inside the dance studio were a good indicator that a class was already in progress. Wondering what lay in store, Bradley and Rex moved nervously towards the sound and gingerly peered through two long, vertical glass strips in a large wooden door. This was all that separated them from the lions' den.

'Did you see that?' barked Bradley.

'What?' asked Rex, scanning the room like a meerkat.

'You see that guy standing on the left by the wall?'

'Er...yes,' replied Rex, catching sight of a tall black man in his mid-twenties.

'Dude, he just jumped up, span around and in mid-air kicked his right-leg straight out. Then, he landed in exactly the same position where he started from. It was awesome!'

This was Steve Brown; it simply had to be. A 6-foot killing machine, able to jump like a jack rabbit and kick like a mule. With his athletic build and aerial grace, aided by his mighty afro, he could easily crush anyone that dared to fight him. He was everything they had imagined, and feared.

Bradley and Rex looked at each other in total desperation. A game of football over on Hackney marshes suddenly seemed a far better way of spending their Sunday morning. The odds of survival were much higher, and at least you got some *free* fruit at half-time.

'Wanna go get some chocolate?' suggested Bradley, deciding the vending area was a much safer place to be right now.

The 1970s vending machine was not like the modern quick-fix hungerwonder it is nowadays, it was an instrument of torture. For starters you had to have exactly the right coins, no change given here. Then you had to decipher the code relating to the snack of your choice. A code so fiendishly difficult that at best, you only ever had a very slim chance of getting what you really wanted in the first place. Finally, a frustrating series of knobs and levers would push you to the point of kicking the machine into submission until it gave up the goods.

On many occasions, Rex had ended up with a safe Kit Kat, instead of the far more exciting Mars bar, due to his complete lack of vending talent. However, the choice of champions was definitely the Marathon bar. If this baby was on display, then its giant alluring presence would easily dwarf all of the other contenders competing for your cash. Nougat, peanuts and caramel, all wrapped in thick milk chocolate - it was the only sensible option. Yummy!

Such was his devotion to this food of kings, Rex was actually quite annoyed when some years later its name was changed to Snickers. Why change perfection?

'What do you want then?' asked Bradley as he fumbled for loose change.

'Marathon,' replied Rex. He was not open to negotiation.

'Okey dokey.'

Okey dokey was definitely NOT the sort of phrase that Steve Brown would use on the mean streets of London. If he did, he would probably be instantly set upon by four or five assailants, all outraged by use of the vocal faux pas. Naturally, each of the unfortunate attackers would then be brutally beaten with well-timed kicks and Kung Fu chops until only blood-soaked bodies lay all around. Steve wouldn't even break into a sweat.

While Rex was visualising the scene, Bradley had already begun the vending procedure. Having made his way through the selection process, he pulled a large handle - one of several to choose from - jammed it back and **bingo!** With the secret code cracked, a trap door opened allowing a Marathon bar to drop to freedom.

Aah, the Marathon bar – the KING of all chocolate snacks. But, much like Roy, it secretly led a double life.

In the UK it was six-inches long, packed with peanuts and dressed in a brown wrapper. This tracing-paper-like wrapper could be removed whole, without tearing, just by gently pulling at the back. As you did so, the wonderful aroma of milk chocolate and roasted peanuts would fill the nostrils. It was pure magic.

However in the U.S., it was dressed in a bright-red wrapper with a ruler printed on the outside. This visual measure proved that inside, it was packing a full eight-inch slab of artery-blocking goodness. But, here is the main difference! The U.S. version didn't originally have the peanuts. It was simply milk chocolate and braided caramel, although it did have an extended length by way of compensation. Rex was happy to sacrifice two inches any day of the week, as long as he kept his nuts.

With the six-inch king of snacks separated into roughly two equal halves, Bradley bit into his half anxiously with no real finesse. Rex carefully removed the top layer of nuts and caramel, only to savour the nougat base in another mouthful. Two different techniques. One taste sensation - Deee-licious!

Heartened by their peanut-packed last meal, the pair headed back to the dance studio, deliberately wandering on the longest alternative route around the leisure centre they could find. Squash, badminton and maybe even trampolining would all be far safer ways of spending their time in this sports facility, but a pact is a pact, so they had to honour it. If either of them reneged on the deal then they would have to explain themselves to Roy, who had promised to fully finance any tuition in the art of killing.

On arrival back at the 'Dance of Death Studio', as Rex had renamed it, there was now a queue of around fifteen people eagerly waiting outside. Some were dressed in black uniforms with a white silk sash tied around the waist, but most were in loose-fitting tracksuit bottoms and white T-shirts. A few were even chatting and laughing. Why, exactly?

The clock on the wall above the notice board displayed 10.59am. Suddenly the large wooden door opened outwards, and a deep voice beckoned everyone inside…

Chapter 9 – Kung Fu Fighting

January 1970

‘My name is Neville. I will be taking the class today.’ The owner of the deep voice had spoken.

NEVILLE???

Rex and Bradley looked at each other in total disbelief. NO!!! He can’t be. This must be a mistake? He was Steve Brown, Kung Fu king, the dark destroyer, the epitome of cool.

The demigod they had feared, as seen earlier performing miracles of aerodynamics, had turned out to be a false prophet named Neville. Yet, if this flying idol was only a mere student, this immediately begged the question: *‘How good is Steve?’*

All those previously waiting by the door outside were now sat on the wooden floor of the dance studio. In front of them, stood a row of eight or nine mean-looking dudes. All dressed in black, with varying colour sashes around their waists - they were your ultimate nightmare.

‘Any first-timers?’ boomed the deep voice.

Rex and Bradley raised their hands in an apologetic manner.

‘Okay, go see Steve over there,’ commanded Neville, nodding towards the corner of the room.

Sat on a chair, behind a small table, was a man who didn’t seem to be that much older than Neville, but somehow, he appeared far more frightening. His head was down, and he was writing in a notebook.

'The rest of you, line up, face me and no talking!' said Neville, instructing in a way that left you in no doubt, **he** was very much the one who was in charge today.

Rex and Bradley apprehensively made their way across the studio towards the real Steve Brown.

'Hello, can we start please?' asked Rex, in a fairly feeble tone, as they approached the table.

'Yeah sure, have you done any martial arts before?' replied Steve, looking up from his notebook.

The pair shook their heads indicating this was definitely not the case.

Steve had spoken, and so far so good, he seemed friendly enough. Rex began to relax a little until suddenly, he noticed the man's huge biceps. These were the guns of Navarone, the sort of thing that made Popeye jealous. On the right-bicep was a tattoo of an arched cobra, with two giant fangs dripping venom as it burst from a skull, ready to strike. The left-bicep was obscured but probably equally as fearsome.

Steve was dressed differently from the others in class. He was wearing a pair of black trousers, silky in appearance, with a white stripe that ran vertically all the way down the outside. His T-shirt was white, embellished with red Chinese writing, and a couple of fierce dragons had been thrown in for artistic intimidation. The words 'Wing Chun Kung Fu' were the sole English letters visible on his chest. Around his waist was the ultimate licence to kill - a black belt. The belt was beautifully knotted on his hip, hanging down his right-side, it demanded respect. This was the mark of certain death. Fear the holder or you may live to regret it - but not for long.

'What are your names?' asked Steve, pen in his hand, poised to add two new students to the class register.

'Rex Roman and Bradley Milwee,' replied Rex on behalf of them both.

Steve looked up again. These were two of the stupidest names he'd ever heard. Was this kid taking the mickey?

'I'm Rex…he's Bradley.'

Steve glared at the two nervous teenagers stood in front of him. One of his eyes looked slightly off-centre, and he had a cold looking stare. This was probably useful for a game of poker, but in this situation it was totally chilling.

A wry smile and a wonky wink broke the tension.

'Okay,' said Steve. 'It's *free* for the first lesson, so see how you like it. Take it easy, and you'll be fine. This is a beginners' class. There's no fighting or contact allowed.'

Oh, sweet music to the ears. *Free* lesson, no contact allowed; they were saved. A welcome sense of relief filled the air with two new students now safe in the knowledge that no one was going to die today.

'My name is Steve Brown, and that student taking the class today is Neville Utaka. He's my chief assistant instructor, but any of the others you saw standing up front, a minute ago, will help you out. This is a club. Everyone is to be respected in here. Do you understand?'

The pair nodded in agreement.

'Right, shoes and socks off, lads. Go join in. Have some fun.'

Barefooted, Bradley and Rex returned to join the class of novice students spread out across the room. Neville was leading them all through various stretching exercises to warm their muscles in preparation for the gymnastics of the forthcoming hour. Thin air and imaginary foes were in for a serious pasting, but at least they wouldn't hit back.

Rex and Bradley would live to fight another day, and so they began their journey into the mysterious world of martial arts. For Rex, the significance of this moment would soon prove a crucial factor in defining his future…

Chapter 10 – Just Desserts

May 1971

It was the 11th of May 1971, and Rex was having a yawn and a scratch as he got out of bed at 102 Roman Way. The winds of change had let one go in Rex's general direction, and the last 18 months had seen him make some big adjustments to his life plan.

Rex and Bradley had both left Winston school with strong grades and gone on to study together at college, on a two-year course. Rex had become more involved in drama at the college although, based on his father's advice from a distance, he was studying maths and science so that he could begin a 'proper' career, working in computers.

"Computers are the future" Rex was told, but, seeing as the average industrial computer was nearly the size of a house - *(without windows)* - he couldn't quite see that happening.

Sadly, Grandad Bill had passed away on the 2nd of May 1970, aged 62. This event had left Rex with a huge hole in his life. Facing his final exams at college, Rex found it impossible to study; the grief was too overwhelming. He was given compassionate leave to re-sit the exams in late October 1970.

Bradley had given up the Kung Fu classes after six months, but he now felt a lot more confident about his personal safety. He had finally banished all of his lingering fears due to the unprovoked attack he'd suffered at the hands of the moronic school bully - Gary Chivers.

Rex had continued his martial arts training with great vigour, learning many new things along the way. Steve Brown was truly an expert in the art of pain, and despite his controlled aggression, Rex was still scared of him. Neville was also a brilliant instructor, but more importantly, he had become a close friend. He and Rex often laughed together about the whole mistaken identity thing before the first-ever lesson, and they spent a lot of time in class as training partners.

Rex realised that the classes were held in the dance studio because the room had mirrors across one wall. His original premonition of blood spilling and dental doom had been wildly exaggerated, as per usual. The simple explanation was that the mirrors enabled the students to see themselves in action and therefore they could improve their technique.

Having officially left college education, Rex was in limbo. He couldn't go to university until the September of 1971, as he had missed his original entry date due to his re-takes. This situation really bothered Ray; he wanted Rex out of the house for once and for all.

Bradley and Rex had decided they were both on a gap year. Lazy days were spent hanging out, playing *Speed Monopoly* and talking nonsense. It was their time to enjoy being young, free from adult pressures.

* * *

Note: Talking nonsense is a particularly interesting pastime. Simply start a conversation, and then improvise with a ridiculous scenario. The one who laughs first, loses the game.

For example:

Rex: Want to go play football tonight?

Bradley: Maybe, if Paul McCartney doesn't ring me again. He keeps begging me for some more song writing tips.

Rex: Yeah, well Miss World keeps on calling me, but I still know who my mates are! (Etc, etc...)

'Mum, I'm going round Bradley's,' said Rex, outside the door of his mother's bedroom, zipping up his jacket, ready to leave.

'Why don't you go out and get a job you lazy git?' shouted Ray from the bottom of the stairs. He was running late for work but couldn't resist any opportunity to make Rex feel unwelcome at home. Their paths didn't often cross in the mornings, so this early verbal abuse was a surprise.

'Why don't you go to work?' responded Rex, in contempt.

This was a red rag to a bull, and Ray rushed up the stairs looking for a fight. He charged at Rex in such a way, it was obvious that physical violence was the only thing on his mind. The pair had always hated each other, and now that Rex was 18-years-old, Ray had figured that it was time to reinforce his alpha male status within the household.

Rex had been regularly studying Kung Fu for 17 months by now. He had never once mentioned it at home. He was very private about his social life and had carefully concealed his favourite hobby. Ray was about to get far more than he had bargained for and was making a big mistake. He arrogantly believed that his superior size and strength would easily quell any resistance to his reign of terror, but today the worm was about to turn.

As Ray moved forward to within striking distance, Rex extended his right-arm at lightning speed straight into his attacker's left-eye socket. The force stopped the advance momentarily, and within seconds, Rex extended his left-fist into the other eye. It all happened so fast that Ray didn't know what had hit him. He held both of his hands to his face as he stumbled around in agony.

Martial arts are about peace, control and inner harmony. They teach self-discipline, respect and that violence is always the very last resort.

Rex ignored all of these principles and was totally consumed with uncontrollable rage. Twelve long and brutal years under Ray's tyrannical rule were being addressed right there on an upstairs landing in Roman Way. To constantly bully a child is unforgivable, and Rex was exacting his revenge, venting his repressed anger.

Noises from the 'Roman v Parker' grudge match shattered the early morning peace and caused both Sandra and Anna to leap from their beds. Knowing this was a contest long overdue, they both came rushing out of their bedrooms to try and calm the explosive situation.

'Stop it! Stop it!' they screamed, almost in unison.

Ray was hurt, but he wasn't out of the fight. Despite his blurred vision, he tried his best to lunge forward for a final assault. As he did so, Rex made a textbook strike straight to Ray's mouth, twisting the punch on execution.

Neville had shown Rex that if you twist a punch, you get increased power on impact with the target. It was all about speed and technique. Unfortunately for Ray, Rex had both.

Ray collapsed to the floor just as Sandra and Anna came to his rescue. Now it really was over. Ray wasn't getting up from such a precise beating, and Rex knew that it was time to leave. Running downstairs and out of the front door, he headed for the safest place he could think of…

* * *

Arriving at Bradley's house, Rex realised that he was shaking as he stood on the front step. The long, forty minute walk had given him time to reflect on the madness that had just occurred. The adrenaline rush had started to leave his body, and now came the aftershock. In addition, his right-hand was bleeding due to a nasty cut on one of his knuckles. He guessed that this was probably caused by the impact on Ray's teeth during the final punch.

Ringing the doorbell, Rex waited for a response.

'Hi Rex, come in,' said Kate as she opened the door. She could tell straight away that there was something very different about the young man standing in front of her.

'What's wrong, hon?' she asked gently, in her soothing American tones.

'I h-had a…' Rex burst into tears. He felt ashamed. He was safe in *this* house, and now he couldn't control his emotions.

Rex had been a regular at chez Milwee during the last four years. In that time he had finally learned to call Bradley's Mum by her first name, Kate, but he still called Roy by the far more respectful title of 'Sir'.

Kate put her arms around Rex to comfort him as Bradley rushed down the stairs to see what was happening.

A short time later as they all sat in the kitchen, Rex started to explain the story of the morning's events, much to Kate and Bradley's horror. They had never even seen where Rex lived, but they had always sensed that he probably endured a difficult time at home.

After Kate had cleaned the blood from the cut, she applied some anti-septic cream and then, finally, a plaster. There was some crazy talk of a trip to the hospital for stitches if this didn't stop the bleeding, but that was Kate just being a Mom. Rex was made to sit with a bag of frozen peas on his hand in order to reduce the swelling around his knuckles.

A lovely cup of hot sweet tea, served with some biscuits, helped to steady the nerves. Despite the frozen produce on his right-hand, Rex deftly switched to his left for some serious dunking action. He greedily consumed nearly a whole packet of chocolate chip cookies in the space of ten minutes, purely for medical reasons you understand.

In the company of two people who really cared about him, Rex spilled his heart out. He found himself talking openly about the years of mental and physical abuse that he'd suffered at the hands of Ray. This was the first time that he'd ever spoken about it to anyone. This was therapy with friends.

'Well, you're not going back there for a few days,' said Kate, her mind firmly made up. 'You can stay here with us for now. Roy will take you back to collect some clothes later.'

'Roy, of course!' What Rex had started, Roy would finish off. A simple clean-up job for the covert operative. Go round the house, take out the trash, cover all tracks and still be home in time for supper. Easy! Roy would tie up all the loose ends and using his extensive underground network, would invent some creative story to explain Ray's sudden disappearance. New motorways and bridges were being built all over Britain, and if Ray ended his days propping up a bridge on the M1, then at least he would have done something useful with his life for a change.

* * *

A car with no wheels, just house bricks for support, was a delightful feature to welcome you to Rex's neighbourhood, and it gave you a good feel for the area's overall quality. Roy parked in an empty space close behind the elevated vehicle, and Rex took a deep breath as he prepared for a showdown.

It was past eight o' clock now, and the usual hoodlums were wandering the area. The residents at Number 99 were having a shouting match, several teenage boys were kicking a football against the wall of Number 105 and at Number 102, the motor-bike, covered in a tarpaulin sheet, indicated that Ray was home.

Rex found something wholly reassuring about knocking on the front door of 102 Roman Way, with a 6-foot, 5-inch giant standing behind him. It was a necessary evil to return home for some clothes and toiletries, but it was still something that Rex had been dreading the whole day.

Ray opened the door and seemed frightened by his visitors. Two black eyes gave him the facial markings of a panda but with none of the cuteness. He also had a front tooth missing. This dental battle scar would serve as a long-term reminder of the morning's failed attack.

'I'm sorry. It was all my fault,' blubbed Ray, bursting into tears.

It was probably the sight of both Roy and Rex on the doorstep that made Ray think more violence was imminent. Ray's normal cocky swagger was gone, and he was almost grovelling with continual apologies as the pair entered the house. This was certainly not the reaction Rex had been expecting. Even so, he sprinted up the stairs to collect his belongings. He didn't have any valuable items in his bedroom, so packing didn't take long. Anything he treasured was safely stored at his grandmother's.

Roy sat in the lounge with Ray, Sandra and Anna while he waited for Rex to collect his things. No one ever did let on what was said in the room that night, but Ray probably got the choice of: "Life or Death?". Subsequently, Ray was never a problem again.

'Ready Mr Milwee, sir,' called Rex from outside the lounge a few minutes later. He didn't want to enter the room as he was desperate to avoid the sight of his tormentor. No further discussion was required. Rex was done here.

Safely back in the car, Rex felt relieved that it was all over. As Roy clipped in his seatbelt, he turned to look at the young man sat beside him. White-faced and nervously clutching a small holdall, Rex obviously wanted to leave the area, so Big Roy uttered some words of comfort...

'Good job, son.'

It is often said that everyone wants to hear three magic words from someone close, and Rex just had. Roy had given him the thumbs up. Coming from a man of Roy's undoubted stature, this felt like a seal of approval and gave Rex a warm glow inside.

Rex had some fresh supplies in his bag, and the worst of the day was over. With Bradley setting up the Monopoly board for another tense game back at chez Milwee, and Kate's amazing apple crumble for supper, things were finally on the up again.

'Gentlemen, start your engines. Let's get out of here.'

* * *

Staying with the Milwee family was merely a short-term solution, but it was a stepping-stone that would lead to a much better place not too far away…

A couple of days later, Rex found himself visiting his grandmother's house, enjoying a milky cup of sweet tea and some of her legendary bread pudding. Newly vocal after his therapy session with Kate and Bradley, he was recounting the story of recent events and life in general at Roman Way. Nan sat there in her favourite armchair, shaking her head, her blood boiling on hearing such news.

'You can come and stay with me if you want to,' offered Nan.

Marie had been living by herself for a year since the death of her darling husband Bill, and after 42-years of marriage and companionship, she was lonely. Rex always was her favourite grandchild, and the pair enjoyed a uniquely close relationship.

'Can I?' asked Rex, in-between mouthfuls of the delicious, *mixture of bread, butter, currants, sugar, bake in an oven for an hour, leave on the side to cool, and then serve,* snack.

'Of course you can!' replied Nan. 'Just pay for some food when you can afford it, and it'll be lovely to have the company.'

Nan made it all sound like it was an entirely obvious thing to do.

So that was the problem solved. Now that he was 18-years-old, Rex could legally break free from his old home to go and live with his beloved Nan. This was a perfect solution for the both of them. Let the good times roll…

'Now, just one more slice of that pudding…'

Chapter 11 – Mission Impossible

Saturday 24th March 1973

It seemed like an ordinary March day back in 1973, but today was destined to become extra-ordinary in so many ways.

Rex was at home with Nan, content just relaxing on the sofa, reading a magazine. An article in it described a new invention called a Video Cassette Recorder which was causing quite a stir as "the must have gadget to own". This technology of the future allowed the user to record up to sixty whole minutes of television by utilising a special tape. A crude timer meant that the lucky owners could even record their favourite programmes while they were out of the house, if they could figure out how to set the thing up in the first place. Rex couldn't believe the genius of this new technology, but at £600 its astronomical price tag made it a play thing for the rich. Rex was anything but rich. He only earned a few pounds a week from teaching martial arts with Neville as Steve expanded his clubs around London.

Rex and Bradley had extended their gap year and never did go away to university. Bradley wanted to play guitar, and London was *the* place to make it, so he decided to stay put. Rex was really happy living with Nan, and for the first time in his life, he had a settled home environment.

Having not long finished his breakfast cereal, Rex was enjoying a cup of tea as he read. He was contemplating whether to launch an early morning assault on the biscuit tin when he was disturbed by an alarmingly loud knock at the front door. Wondering who it was, Rex crept towards the door with some haste until he recognised the profile dancing on his front step.

'Rex, you have got to come with me,' panted the familiar figure before the door was even fully opened. He was in a hyperactive state and beckoning Rex towards him.

'Hey Bradley, what's going on?'

'Today, I am going to change your life, my friend. You will never forget this day…ever!'

Coming from Bradley, this was a bold statement. He had already renamed Rex and helped to rehouse him, so now what did he have planned? Funnily enough, it's often said that big things do come along in 3s, so something was bound to be just around the corner.

'Pink Floyd release *The Dark Side of the Moon* today, and we're going to get it right now,' said Bradley, urging Rex outside.

'Pink who?'

'No time to waste, dude. Come on, come on!'

Bradley was getting agitated by the speed of progress - or lack of it.

'Come in, I'll get ready.'

Rex motioned his restless friend inside. Any trip to the moon was going to have to wait until the breakfast remains were cleared away and appropriate clothing was selected for such a lunar expedition.

'Hi Nan…how you doing?' asked Bradley as he entered the lounge, only to start pacing up and down.

Bradley had a real fondness for the sweet old lady sitting in the armchair by the window. Glasses perched on the end of her nose, she was busily knitting a jumper that Rex was never going to wear. Her favourite pastime made her happy, as did having company in the house.

'Hello young Bradley,' said Nan, looking up. 'Do you want something to eat, dear?'

'No, thank you,' replied the impatient guest.

There must be something about Nan DNA the world over that triggers similar behaviour patterns upon reaching a certain age. When anyone enters their home, the genetic urge kicks in, and food must immediately be offered to any guest. There isn't a Nan anywhere that will take 'No' for an answer.

'Bread pudding? Fairy cake? I've got some lovely fresh ham in the fridge.'

Nan really wasn't listening to Bradley's polite *"no thank you"*. She started to get up from her chair, eager to prepare some food for her guest.

'Go on, take a fairy cake with you,' she insisted.

'We're off out now,' said Rex, leaning over Nan before she could fully rise from her seat. 'See you later.'

He kissed her tenderly on the forehead to say goodbye and whispered gently in her ear: 'Nice try.'

Nan sunk back into her chair - defeated. She knew the battle to offload the surplus stock of fairy cakes was lost.

* * *

Bradley was now 21-years-old and had recently passed his driving test. He had a gorgeous red Mini with the number 14 emblazoned on each of the side doors. No one knew why, but there was probably a reason.

'I've got something to play you in the car,' said Bradley as they reached the vehicle.

'Okay,' replied Rex, wondering if Bradley had recorded some of the songs he had been writing recently.

Inside the car, Bradley had a proposition...
'Let's play a game of Mission Impossible. If you can get to Charlie's Record Box without nodding your head in joy once, then I will give you a crisp five pound note for completing the two minute task.'

'Oookkaaaaayyyy...' Rex suspiciously confirmed his interest, knowing there was a catch.

'However, your total lack of musical taste will sadly mean that we can no longer be friends. By the way, once you've got the cash, your seat will self-destruct in five seconds.'

Rex had a quick think...
'Five quid!!!...five...hang on! Did he just say my seat will explode?'

Bradley laid out his terms... 'And if I see any nodding during the drive then you owe me a Marathon bar, plus, I get a one thousand pound head start in the next game of Monopoly.'

'Right, move once, it costs me the king of snacks and a grand in Monopoly money. Sit still, lose my best friend, but I get a fiver as a parting gift, oh and blown-up if I don't get out of the car fast enough. Hmmm...tough one.'

'Deal! Do your worst and let the best man win,' said Rex, taking the bet. He was feeling lucky.

Rex was almost expecting a choir of angels and a blinding light as Bradley held a cassette tape in the air. This was THE ultimate representation of the very latest in audio technology. The car, complete with a cassette player, had been Roy's way of celebrating Bradley's 21st birthday. It was a big number, and this was a big present.

To build suspense, Bradley moved the cassette slowly towards the player, having previously cued a song to exactly the right position for maximum effect. He was not prepared to lose this bet or his friend. With the tape inserted, the stereo sprang to life with a disturbing message...

"One of These Days I'm Going to Cut You into Little Pieces"

Gulp! *'Cut me into pieces?…Roy?…Oh my…'* Before Rex could even finish connecting the Chain of Doom, the sonic energy filling the car sent him on another line of thought. *'Who is this? This is the greatest sound I've ever heard.'*

Rex tried his best to resist moving an inch, but inside his head that oh-so fertile mind was in overdrive...
'Bradley's been my closest friend for six years...but five pounds is a lot of cash. It's also a lot of note...the size of a small blanket. Oh, those drums...that guitar...this is hopeless...just give in. Get rocking!'

Before the journey was even halfway complete, the two of them were nodding their heads like a pair of demented wood-peckers. The driving beat and slide guitar had proven an irresistible combination as the Mini zoomed its way through London, on route to its final destination.

Rex had severe neck ache as the car came to rest up outside Charlie's Record Box. They could have easily walked there, but that wasn't part of Bradley's master plan. With the music stopped and the ignition off, Bradley smiled one of those 'told you so' smiles as he turned to face Rex. It had all gone entirely as Bradley had predicted; talk about taking candy from a baby! This was the easiest Marathon bar and Monopoly money he had ever won.

Bradley was a music buff. He followed all of the latest news about bands, concerts and album release dates. Today was a red-letter day in his calendar, and one which he had been eagerly anticipating for some time.

Rex was a Jimi Hendrix fan, but then again who wasn't? This new sound was something different though; something he hadn't expected.

'Who was that?' quizzed Rex, he had to know.

'Pink Floyd,' explained Bradley. '**They** are the reason we're here today,' he stated, nodding towards the shop to their left. 'I know to most people that this shabby building looks like a run-down record store, owned by a fat hippy with appalling personal hygiene, but guess what…THIS will be where you become a devotee of Roger, David, Nick and Rick.'

'Who?' asked Rex, puzzled again.

'Pink Floyd! They're the band members. Come on Rex, keep up.'

With the first-leg of the mission complete, the most important part was about to follow…

Chapter 12 – Charlie's Record Box

Saturday 24th March 1973

Charlie's Record Box was not a fancy store run by a faceless corporation. It was run, rather unsurprisingly, by Charlie.

A blue sign over the shopfront displaying the words:

CHARLIE'S RECORD BOX

was easily the best clue to its whereabouts if you were trying to find it. A few posters stuck in the front window, advertising the latest and greatest record releases of the times, also helped.

A small bell above the inside of the door would ding-a-ling to let Charlie know when a customer had entered his shop. It was probably one of the most inactive bells in London.

'Right on time,' said Charlie as the ding-a-ling worked like a charm.

'Of course,' Bradley replied. 'I've been waiting for this day for weeks.'

Charlie knew Bradley well; he was a regular customer, and one of the few still keeping him in business. The pair of them had planned this day with military precision, and their anxious wait was nearly over.

'And who might this be?' enquired Charlie.

'This is Rex, he's my best friend. I just introduced him to Floyd in the car on the way over here.'

'What track?'

'**One of These Days**,' replied Bradley, looking smug about his selection.

'Ooh, nice choice,' approved Charlie as though it were a fine wine. 'Sooo, he has yet to sample the delights of **Several Species of Small Furry Animals Gathered Together in a Cave and Grooving with a Pict?'**

Charlie laughed loudly and looked even smugger than Bradley. This was Nerd Tennis, a game where the players bat trivia backwards and forwards, as opposed to a ball, each trying to outdo the other with their encyclopedic knowledge. This was much more of a friendly exhibition match rather than full competition, but even so, Charlie had just served an ace and burnt a sizeable hole in Bradley's racquet.

'I love nature programmes,' said Rex, thinking that the BBC needed a much catchier title for its furry animal documentaries.

The players rolled their eyes and called time on the game.

'So much to learn,' sighed Charlie as he cleaned his glasses in victory.

Bradley didn't have the heart to tell Rex that this tongue twister was actually one of Pink Floyd's stranger, and longer, song titles. He knew that Charlie was merely demonstrating that **he** was the fountain of all knowledge when it came to the Floyd. Such details were completely lost on Rex, as before the car ride, he wasn't even aware of the band.

'Right, I'll shut the store for five minutes,' announced Charlie. 'We'll all share this moment together. This is a special day in musical history.'

As Charlie came out from behind the shop counter, Rex caught full sight of him for the first time. Ill-fitting clothes barely managed to contain a portly frame, and his brown hair had been scraped back into a long pony tail. Charlie also had a large stain collection down the front of his T-shirt: a faded garment that doubled as a comprehensive guide to the world of condiments - this man was clearly a connoisseur of sauce.

Walking past Rex and Bradley towards the front door, Charlie left a vapour trail behind him. It wasn't pleasant. It was one nasty niff. Either Charlie needed a bath and a change of clothes, or he was wearing some cheap French aftershave:

Le Skunk pour l'homme.

Once the door was locked and the Open sign turned to Closed, Charlie waddled back to behind the counter, panting from the effort.

'Here it is, man,' said Charlie as he held up the album.

The artwork was both striking and unique. It had an all black background with a white-edged triangle in the centre, and a single beam of white light entered only for a rainbow spectrum to exit. It seemed to resemble the refracting light prism design, which Rex had seen before in his science books at college.

Bradley and Rex were both transfixed by the sight.

'Now we carefully remove the shrink-wrap,' said Charlie, in a surgeon-like manner. He was taking this operation very, very seriously.

As the wrapping came off, the gatefold cover opened to reveal a magical transcript.

'Ooh, lyrics!' Charlie's eyes lit up as he noticed the six columns of intellectual poetry laid out before him. 'That's a first.'

Removing the vinyl disc from its inner sleeve and then placing it gently on the record player, Charlie gave the impression that he was savouring every second. Bradley became ever more excited as the record began...

A heartbeat pumped through the speakers, then some clocks, then a voice, now a cash register, ooh and another, followed by some laughter, now a big crescendo of sound and finally the drums came in...there must have been a kitchen sink in there somewhere...this was awesome!

Three enthralled listeners were huddled closely around the open record cover on the counter top, all desperate to read the lyrics in time with the singing. Being too close to Charlie wasn't a good place to be, but maybe this was a test of devotion. If so, it was a tough one.

Rex was breathing through his mouth so that the oxygen didn't have to filter through his nostrils, bringing with it Charlie's ripe scent.

Some 2 minutes and 26 seconds after the music had started, the singing began…

"Breathe, breathe in the air…don't be afraid to care"

Bradley and Rex looked at each other; there was definitely some irony in this situation. They were both actually very afraid to breathe at that moment in time. To not be afraid could be described as reckless and may lead to temporary blindness.

'Brilliant!' exclaimed Bradley as the song ended. 'I'll take it.'

Charlie left the record playing as he sold Bradley a fresh new copy of this majestic album. This one had the shrink-wrapping intact, which meant that the magical experience of opening the record could be enjoyed again. He announced that his store was going to remain closed for 'study purposes', and it was time to crack open the snacks, none of them healthy or low calorie.

The aptly named **On the Run** began blasting around the shop. Rex and Bradley were keen to embrace this running concept, mainly to get some fresh air into their lungs, so they made their excuses and left.

'Man, this is gonna be a classic,' gasped Bradley once he and Rex were both safely outside. 'We've got to stay home tonight and listen to this record in full. Come to my place for seven o'clock. No excuses.'

'Absolutely,' confirmed Rex.

'We need beer,' said Bradley, looking to further enhance their evening. 'I'll see if Roy has any stock we can liberate for the good of mankind.'

'Great idea. I'll bring the fairy cakes.'

'Dude, I was thinking something more along the line of nuts. Definitely a salt-based snack.'

Rex had tried his best, but it looked like Nan was going to have real trouble shifting stock.

'Bradley?'

'Yeeessssss,' replied Bradley as he gazed lovingly at the record cover.

'You won't start without me, will you?' asked Rex, concerned that Bradley now owned the album, and there was still over eight hours to go until their scheduled get together.

'What kind of a friend do you think I am? As if I could, that's unthinkable. It would be like never wearing flares again, just because someone decided they weren't fashionable anymore. Never gonna happen.'

'Oh good,' said Rex, agreeing that such a fall from grace was pretty unthinkable. Talk about a cast-iron guarantee! Everyone knew that flares would last forever!!! It was obvious that Bradley intended to keep his word.

As luck would have it, today was a Saturday. Kate and Roy had made plans to go to the cinema that evening, meaning the house would be empty for a few hours. This would provide the perfect opportunity to listen to the album in full, probably several times, and drink large quantities of beer with maybe a few salty snacks thrown in for good measure.

How did Bradley do it? What was his secret? Once again he had opened a new door for Rex to walk through. Bradley's earlier premonition of a life-changing experience had come true with startling accuracy. Today was the first time that Rex had ever heard of Pink Floyd, and now...

He was absolutely hooked!

Chapter 13 – A Confession

Saturday 24th March 1973

It certainly seemed like a long wait that day until the 7pm premiere of *The Dark Side of the Moon* at Bradley's. Rex had promised to help Nan with some gardening, and keeping his word, he stayed at home. He had a ham sandwich for lunch, followed by a fairy cake and washed it all down with a cup of tea. He was doing his bit.

As the hour of reckoning approached, Rex changed into his best going-out clothes, after watching the 5.30pm edition of *The Wombles. (That Great Uncle Bulgaria was one clever Womble! More of a guru than a furry stop-motion character living on Wimbledon Common.)*

Rex kissed Nan goodbye as she handed him a goody bag of food, and he left. He walked to Bradley's full of excitement, wondering what musical treats lay in wait.

* * *

'Hi Rex, come in,' said Kate as she opened the front door. 'He's in the lounge.'

Rex entered the house and took off his shoes, placing them neatly by the door. Roy was in the hall, wearing his standard issue CIA trench coat.

'Hey Rex.'

'Hello sir,' Rex replied, wondering if Roy was packing any concealed weapons under his coat or having a day off from murder, seeing as it *was* the weekend.

'Right, we're off out now. I've made up a bed in the spare room if you want to stay over,' said Kate in her typical caring, motherly manner.

'Thank you,' replied Rex, before heading into the lounge.

'Have a good time you two,' shouted Kate as she and Roy left for the evening. Their departure signalled the start of a lads' night in and meant that the stereo could be turned up full-blast for the next few hours.

Bradley was sat on a stool strumming his guitar, oblivious to the arrival of his one man audience. Rex was admiring his friend's musical talent until his attention was distracted by two giant tins of beer. They were sat on top of the coffee table like gifts to the Gods, soon to sacrificed in the name of rock 'n' roll.

These *gifts* were actually in the form of Party Seven tins. Not content with a regular can, some genius at Watney's had conceived a novel way of packing a better product. Not one, not two; don't even waste your time with a feeble three pint effort. No, each of these bad boys contained seven pints of the finest beer the brewery had to offer - in one oversized tin! To avoid the creative use of a screwdriver and a rolling pin, Roy had fitted a special tap to one of the tins to aid the extraction of its refreshing golden liquid. The other tin had a date with a screwdriver later, once the first bad boy had been dispatched.

'That sounds great,' said Rex, genuinely impressed by the guitar playing, as Bradley concluded his set.

'Thanks, man.'

'Is that one of your songs?' asked Rex. 'I really like it.'

'I thought you might.'

'You should really try and do something with your guitar playing, mate. I remember when I first heard you at school, you were amazing.'

'Yeah, I wanna make it as a rock star. Wouldn't that be cool?'

An ambitious comment, destined to lead to another adventure, another day.

Bradley never did get around to telling Roy that Milwee was an awful surname, but then again only a very brave man would. The fictional Bradley Mills never did graduate from Winston school after all.

'So, where's the record?' asked Rex. 'I can't wait any longer.' The notorious wild man was keen to get the party started.

'Here it is,' replied Bradley, handing over the album. Rex was so overawed by its attractive design that he completely failed to notice the absence of the shrink-wrap.

'Now *this* is fabulous.'

'Isn't it just,' concurred Bradley. 'Check out the lyrics.'

Rex started to read some of the words printed on the inside cover. One song in particular, caught his eye...

"New car…caviar…football teams…Lear jets"

This sounded perfect, with the exception of the caviar, but then the band probably couldn't think of a decent rhyme for Frosties. All the good stuff Rex could have if he actually had any cash, which of course he didn't.

'I really want to listen to this one,' said Rex, pointing to the lyrics of **Money.**

'Rex, this is a concept album. Its true genius can only be appreciated if you start at the beginning, then listen all the way through to the end without stopping. It's a forty-three minute musical tapestry of sonic beauty and enlightenment. It's a complete journey, not some bus you hop on halfway through a tour.'

'How do you know?'

'Er…I read it in the newspaper,' replied Bradley, looking away guiltily.

'Oh, I see.'

Rex was never going to make it as a detective. A life in the police force was one to cross straight off his career list, although he did like all the police themed programmes on the television. Rex often missed the blindingly obvious right in front of him.

As Rex grabbed the giant bag of Jungle Fresh peanuts that Kate had left for them, he prepared to empty the contents into a large bowl on the coffee table.

'You sort out the food and drink,' said Bradley, assigning jobs. 'I'll start the record on side two then, you barbarian.'

'Okey dokey,' replied Rex. *'Oh dear! Did I just say "okey dokey"? NO! Please say I didn't…I can't believe it. Neville must never know.'*

Being so appalled at his casual stroll into a vocal no-go area, Rex completely missed the bowl and emptied the family size bag of nuts onto the carpet.

'Bradley? Have you got a Hoover or something?' asked Rex, conscious of the large quantity of salty Jungle Freshness strewn across the floor.

'Why?...oh, I see...nah, don't worry about it. We'll scoop the stuff off the top and what we don't eat, I'll clean up later.'

Rex poured two pints of beer and opened the goody bag that Nan had given him. Not particularly partial to carpet food, Rex decided that he was going to have a fairy cake with his beer after all. The sight of the glacé cherry on top of the icing sugar totally clinched the deal.

As the pair settled down to a rock 'n' roll evening full of Pink Floyd, beer, peanuts and fairy cakes, they both felt pretty content about their Saturday night. Hearing the opening bars of **Money**, they sensed that something truly magical was upon them.

Cash registers ping-ponged from speaker to speaker as the bass guitar laid down a filthy groove. The sofa became an altar, and the band played on...

* * *

'I feel a bit dizzy,' groaned Rex, a mere 6 minutes and 23 seconds later as the song faded, only to segue into the next piece of the musical tapestry.

'You lightweight! You haven't even had a whole pint yet,' jeered Bradley, trying to hide his disgust before he realised: *'Less for Rex, more for me!'*

'Yeah, well, I don't drink much.'

'Why not?' Bradley was bemused as he poured another tall one.

'I never wanted to be like Ray I guess, you know - an alcoholic.'

Rex had never even mentioned Ray since the day he left home. It must have been the beer loosening his tongue.

'Oh Rex, you don't smoke, you're rubbish at drinking and you live with your Nan. You're really not cut out for rock 'n' roll, are you?'

'Guess not,' agreed Rex as the room started to spin a little.

Rex's career list had been decimated over the past few years. He couldn't stand the sight of blood or needles, so *Doctor* had been struck off. He was often susceptible to motion sickness, so the *First British Man in Space* was never going to blast off from the launch pad. And now, he clearly couldn't take his beer, oh and had no money, so *International Playboy* was a complete non-starter.

Rex had an idea about what he wanted to do with his life, but he knew it was an impossible dream. Still, it just wouldn't go away.

Bradley grabbed his freshly extracted pint and downed the whole lot in one hit…

Buuuuuuurrrrrpppppppppp!!!!!!! Aaaahhhhh!!!

'That's one small beer for man, one giant burp for mankind.'

This was Bradley's contribution to advancing science.

Rex looked on in distaste before plucking up the courage to make a huge confession...

'I want to be an actor, Bradley.'

'Good for you, man. That's a brilliant idea.'

'Thanks, mate.'

'Well, that was easy,' thought Rex. A long held dream had finally been vocalised thanks to the liquid-based support of Watney's brewery.

'Two beer or not two beer, that is the question,' said Bradley, reciting his favourite Shakespearean quote. 'Whether it is nobler to drink it all and suffer outrageous burping or to take arms against a sea of peanuts.'

'That's not right,' argued Rex, fully aware of the proper text.

'That's Jazz Shakespeare. C'mon relax, don't get all arty on me.'

'I don't think I should drink anymore tonight,' whined Rex, his head wobbling uncontrollably on his neck.

'Tell you what,' said Bradley, in a deal making frame of mind. 'As a special favour, I'm gonna save you from this evil liquid and consume it myself, just so that Roy doesn't think you're a complete girl.'

'You're the best,' slurred Rex.

'No, don't thank me. Let's just say you owe me a favour. Now, let's start this album from the beginning. Let's do this the way it's supposed to be done.'

As Bradley began the record from the start of side one, Rex put his feet up on the sofa in a vain attempt to stop the room from spinning further.

A heartbeat pumped through the speakers as the music began. Free from the pungent stench of Charlie, Rex was able to study the awesome sound a lot closer…

'What's that ticking?…Did someone just swear?…What on earth's he laughing at? Why is she screaming? What's going on in there?… aah, the drums have started, what a sound…I'm going to enjoy this… oh boy, that beer is really getting to me…I feel all…' Zzzzzzzzzz

To complete a vintage performance Rex promptly had a sneaky snooze, only to be woken from his peaceful slumber some seven minutes later. The album had reached the song **Time** and a series of ringing alarm clocks were belting out of the speakers. Startled by the loud sound Rex woke up, fell off the sofa and landed face down in the peanuts. Rex survived his 18-inch fall, brushed off the nutty facepack and then listened to the complete album several times during the evening. At the end of the night he came to one simple conclusion…

'This is the greatest album of all-time.'

Chapter 14 – Don't Buy A Fake

Saturday 16th November 1974

18 months later, Rex was undertaking some serious study in the fine art of acting, with the aim of one day going professional. The pivotal moment of confession at Bradley's, while under the alcoholic influence of at least half a pint of the strong stuff, had fired the starting gun for change.

He had enrolled in a drama club, attended acting workshops and even managed to perform in a few amateur plays. The thespian ambition, first born in Winston school, was now being nurtured. Bradley showed his support by saying that Rex certainly had a natural flair for a bit of drama.

Rex had already perfected three American regional accents, all of them from Alabama, courtesy of his favourite cartoon chicken - Foghorn Leghorn. Sadly, Rex had set fresh new lows in Shakespearean drama. His tragic *Hamlet* was cruelly labelled *"Omelette"* by the critics, but at least he was trying.

Living with Nan meant that Rex didn't need much money as she took good care of him. The money he did earn came from working for his friend Neville. Steve Brown had opened some new Kung Fu clubs around London; such was the growing interest in martial arts. As a result, Neville had been promoted to the head instructor at Islington Sports & Leisure Centre. Rex held the position of chief assistant, on account of his talent.

Bradley had managed to form a band. He was often writing songs and rehearsing with the boys in the hope of hitting the big time. Music was the love of Bradley's life; Rex felt the same about acting. They were both now in their early 20s, with aspirations of fame and fortune in the performing arts.

Abba had recently won the Eurovision song contest, but Rex couldn't see them getting anywhere. Sure they were the high priests of fashion with those platform shoes and fancy jumpsuits but come on - a song about a railway station? Mamma Mia!

Steve Austin, *The Six Million Dollar Man*, was providing artistic inspiration with his super human feats on television. Rex would often perform heroic actions in perfect slow-motion, much to Bradley's amusement.

Pink Floyd, meanwhile, were scheduled to play some concerts at Wembley Empire Pool from the 14th - 17th of November. Some years later the venue changed its name to Wembley Arena, which didn't annoy Rex half as much as when the Marathon bar was renamed Snickers. What **was** the point of that exactly?

Roy had secured two tickets for Bradley and Rex to attend the musical event of the year. Rex didn't ask how many people Roy had threatened in order to obtain front row seats for the Saturday night, he was just happy to accept his *free* ticket.

If you ever find yourself attending a concert at Wembley, public transport is by far the best way to get there. When you come out of the London Underground station at Wembley Park, walk down the hill, and in less than no time you will arrive at the venue. If you are confused, then mingle with the masses and you'll either end up at a concert or on one hell of a pub crawl!

On this particular November night in 1974, Bradley was lost and looking for someone to follow. He knew that anyone with long hair, a denim jacket and large sideburns made a fairly safe bet. As he got closer to the venue, all manner of street vendors and illegal touts were operating in the area. Many of them were trying to sell poor quality merchandise to those looking to save a few quid, but it's common knowledge that only an absolute idiot would purchase goods from these scoundrels.

'Ooh look, Bradley. T-shirts!' Rex said excitedly.

A street tout, with a large quantity of black T-shirts slung over his right-forearm, had clearly seen Rex coming. He had a vast array of watches on his left-forearm, presumably as a back-up trade in case the T-shirt sales were a bit slow.

'Tickets, buy or sell, special edition tour T-shirts,' he shouted, hoping some dimwit would soon be tempted into making a purchase.

Rex stood surveying the tatty merchandise.

'Don't do it, man. They're not worth the money, get one inside,' said Bradley, through gritted teeth, his back turned to the tout.

'But it's all part of my cash flow plan. The money I save here can be diverted towards other concert related treats.'

'What treats?' asked Bradley.

'Ah, you will see. All in good time, my friend. It's all part of a cunning plan.'

As the pair looked at the T-shirts on the hairy rail, Bradley noticed that something was a bit odd about the stock in this open air clothing boutique.

'Rex, they're fakes! Just look at that one!!!' pleaded Bradley, pointing at a dodgy design in disgust. A black T-shirt, laid out flat on some cardboard, seemed authentic enough at first with its rainbow spectrum colours. However, the iconic triangle, as made famous on the cover of *The Dark Side of the Moon* album, had been replaced by a large square.

'Fakes?' the tout looked hurt by this accusation. 'Fakes? No, no my young friends. These are the finest T-shirts ever made, lads. Selling like hot cakes these are. No more room in the venue, so they sent me out here to sell 'em. Special edition these are, just for this tour.'

Pigs could have easily done a fly-past at that moment in honour of this gigantic whopper of a statement, but that's another story for later.

'That's not even the right design,' said Bradley in a dismissive tone, not buying the hype for a second.

'If you are referring to the unique artwork on the front, then you need to remember this is actually the live tour T-shirt, which…I will agree…does indeed differ slightly from the album cover. This square represents the stage, you see. No band plays on a triangle, do they?'

'Good point, he's right about that,' agreed Rex. 'How much?'

'50p. They're two quid inside, on account of venue taxes.'

'Dude, this is a waste of money. Don't do it,' begged Bradley in a last ditch attempt to save Rex from himself.

'50p Bradley, 50p! That's a bargain, and I'll still have some money left. Plus, I get to look cool at the gig. It's a done deal.'

Rex handed over the money as Bradley shook his head in disbelief.

It was interesting to note that as a policeman approached, the tout suddenly had other places to be.

Wembley Empire Pool is not known for its acoustic perfection. It is a giant, ugly concrete-shed of a building shaped in a long rectangle, that can hold anywhere between 8-9000 people, depending on seating arrangements. Tonight was going to be a sell-out gig in front of an adoring crowd.

Once safely inside the shed, Rex and Bradley were happily soaking up the charged atmosphere. They had made a point of arriving early so they could enjoy the pre-show ambience in the venue. This was their first Pink Floyd concert, and they both wanted to enjoy every minute of the evening.

Rex revealed the second part of his plan…

'You see, the money I saved on a T-shirt, I can now spend on food. Brilliant!'

'Oh Rex, you are a genius,' said Bradley, sarcastically.

'I thank you.'

As previously witnessed, sometimes Rex Roman could be a real plonker.

Ironically for Rex, this tatty T-shirt would play a central role to the next part of the evening. He was about to experience the most important moment of his life, and it had nothing to do with music…

Chapter 15 – Splat!!!

Saturday 16th November 1974

Rex Roman is a very simple man when it comes to food. He has a few favourite food choices and is quite happy eating nothing else. He never seems to tire of these basic provisions.

Cereal is the Number One choice; mainly as there are so many different types. Anytime of the day, cereal makes a tasty snack. If there's cold weather outside, then have it with hot milk. If the weather's hot, mild or maybe even slightly overcast with a 20% chance of showers, then have it with cold milk instead. If there's no milk to be found, then simply grab a handful and eat it 'au naturel'. The versatility of cereal knows no bounds.

Baked beans on toast. Well, not actually on the toast as the hot beans make the toast go soggy, and that's just not cricket. No, in truth it's baked beans *with* toast as the beans are placed on one plate, the toast on another. A very small and subtle difference, but one that's essential for such a gourmet feast.

Marathon bars. Aah, the classic. Enough said.

A hot dog with fried onions, all covered in a generous helping of tomato ketchup. Now this is a special treat. Not the sort of thing usually eaten at home, this particular snack is best enjoyed at: fairgrounds, sporting events and of course… ROCK CONCERTS!

'Ooh look, Bradley. Hot dogs! I love hot dogs, you want one?' asked Rex, his mind already made up about his next meal. The joy of his latest discovery saw Rex pointing at the hot dog stand, like a thirsty man in a dessert spotting an oasis.

Having saved money buying a dodgy T-shirt, Rex now had the extra cash for a hot dog. What a strategy; the man was as bright as a button.

'Are you kidding?' asked Bradley. 'Dude, do you know what actually goes into those things?'

'Taste from heaven?' replied Rex, feeling guilty he had even seen them.

'Roy says they sweep the abattoir floors for the contents. It's all the stuff they don't use in anything else. It's road kill in a bun, Rex.'

'That's a no then, is it?'

'Of course it's a no!' Bradley had made his point.

Under normal circumstances just hearing the words *'Roy'* and *'abattoir'* in the same sentence, Rex would have started connecting 'The Chain'. Unusually, all doom related thoughts were currently suspended, on account of hunger.

'Can I have one?' begged Rex, feeling he needed permission to purchase.

'Yeah, go ahead. I can't even bear to watch you eat it. I'm gonna go look at the merchandise over there. Come meet me when you're done.' Bradley had pointed to the 'official' merchandise stand where all manner of tour souvenirs were being sold.

'Will do,' said Rex, making a mental note of the meeting point. He charged off towards the hot dog stand, rubbing his hands together in glee. *"Come to Daddy"* he chuckled as he considered the genius of his plan.

Approaching the oasis, Rex could tell that this was obviously a premier vendor. To the right of the stand was a table with a collection of plastic bottles, colour coded to aid selection of the perfect condiment, to further enhance the delicious snacks on sale. In the red bottles - the all-time classic: *tomato ketchup*. Next to these stood the alternative brown bottles containing the less popular but still tasty: *brown sauce*. Finally, there were the yellow bottles. These contained: *mustard*. Not one of Rex's favourites but a treat for those of a more adventurous nature.

Rex was a stock standard tomato ketchup man. On arrival at the stand, he got in line to wait his turn.

'Yes, mate?'

'Hot dog, please. With extra onions,' said Rex.

'Wanna drink wiv that?'

'Coke with ice, please,' asked Rex, politely.

'Wiv ice? Do what?...oh, lah-di-dah...don't sell it wiv ice, mate. Just in the cans. Do you want one, or not?' barked the vendor, full of East London charm.

'Er...yes...okay, thanks.'

'Wiv ice,' *...tut!...*'what a princess,' muttered the vendor, not familiar with such difficult customers.

Trading money for the goods, Rex now had his hands full of gastronomic promise.

In his left-hand was the greatest snack known to mankind. Sumptuous choice cuts of the finest meat, all prepared by expert chefs in sterilised kitchens. These were then wrapped in a long bun, made from wheat grown in fields, where laughing children would merrily skip as they played in golden sunshine. Finally on top sat a mountain of fried onions which were so sweet, that not a single tear had been shed in their preparation.

In his right-hand was a fountain of refreshment, without ice.

Turning to his right to select the sauce of his choice from the table, Rex was only one squirt away from heaven.

SPLAT!!!

Rex looked down at his chest. With both hands occupied, he was frozen to the spot and not prepared for what he saw. A wet patch had appeared on his new T-shirt, it was bright red, so dark thoughts ran through his mind…

'Blood is red. I asked for ice and offended the vendor. Now he is exacting a bloody revenge, only to put me in future hot dogs as the main ingredient. I'm too young to die. Bradley was right all along. Why didn't I listen to him?…WHYYYYYYYYY????????'

Rex dropped to his knees, convinced this was the end. His head was tilted back towards the heavens as he waited for the pain from his chest wound to kick in. Amazingly, he managed to hold on to his food and drink, determined to take them with him on his journey to the afterlife.

The normal Chain of Doom service had resumed.

All of a sudden, the voice of an angel stopped it from connecting any further...

'I am so sorry. Oh no, look at your T-shirt!'

Rex looked up to see his second vision of the day. First he had seen the hog dog stand, a vision of high cuisine. Now in front of him stood a vision of loveliness, the like of which he had never seen before.

'I can see you've got your hands full. Here, let me wipe that for you.'

Rex was too tongue-tied to respond to the sensible offer. Slightly embarrassed by his dramatic collapse only moments before, he clambered to his feet with his mouth open and heart pounding at the sight of his assailant. In front of him stood a beautiful, young, slender goddess with a huge smile, flawless complexion and long, slightly curly, brown hair. She also had the deepest brown eyes that Rex had ever seen. Her voice sounded wonderful and armed with some napkins, she started wiping off the ketchup splattered across Rex's chest.

'I am so sorry about this, I really am. I was just putting some tomato ketchup on my hot dog when…I really don't know what happened…I gave the bottle a good squeeze, the bottle farted and the ketchup just flew out. I am really, really sorry.'

'That's okay,' mumbled Rex, too entranced to care.

'It's not okay. I've ruined your T-shirt. I am such an idiot. It's such an unusual design, too. Wow! Really unusual. Can I buy you a new one?'

'If you want to,' replied Rex, thinking any extra time in her devine company would be a bonus.

'Yes, I do want to. It would make me feel much better.'

'Okay, thanks.'

'Do you want to eat your hot dog first?' she asked.

'Oh right, hot dog!' thought Rex as he returned from his trance. Having been so smitten with the heavenly vision before him, he had completely forgotten about the prized bounty he was holding.

'I love this band,' she said as the last of the napkins were thrown into a near-by rubbish bin.

'Me too.'

'And I just love hot dogs,' she said, taking a big bite out of her own snack.

'Me too,' confirmed Rex. He was a master of conversation.

It is often said, the secret to success in love is to have things in common with a partner. With Pink Floyd and hot dogs already in the bank, this was a promising start.

'What's your name?' she asked.

'My name is Rex…Rex Roman,' he replied, wondering if it was best to avoid the onions.

'Rex Roman. Well it's nice to meet you Rex and, er…sorry again about your T-shirt.'

'What's you name?' asked Rex.
(The master was finally up and running.)

'Promise you won't laugh.'

'I won't laugh…promise.'
(He was hitting top gear now.)

'My name is Lucy.'

'Lucy...that's a lovely name, why would I laugh at that?'
(Go Rex, Go!)

'Lucy Doggitt.'

Just prior to this formal introduction, Rex had unfortunately taken a large swig of his drink. Reacting to the surname, he couldn't contain his laughter. However, having a mouthful of cola caused an immediate problem. As he felt too ashamed to spit the liquid out, it only had one way to go. The drink dribbled down through his nostrils as he began to choke.
(Rex was back on the hard shoulder of the road to romance, with the hazard lights flashing and the bonnet up.)

'That's attractive,' giggled Lucy, admiring the sight of the nasal waterfall.

'I'm sorry...it just...it just went down the wrong hole, that's all. I wasn't laughing at your name,' lied Rex between coughs and splutters.

'It's okay. I know it's awful. One day, if I meet someone special, I'll get married and finally be rid of it.'

'Aha, so she's single. Time to really turn it on...'

'What's the name of your first pet?' enquired Rex, thinking he had a solution to the identity crisis. 'You know, dog or cat, proper pet. Goldfish don't count.'

'Well years ago, my parents had a bulldog called Spike. Why?'

'Never mind,' said Rex, knowing this avenue of conversation was closed.

Over the next few minutes, while Rex finished his meal, he discovered some new things about Lucy.

Firstly, Lucy liked to talk. She liked to talk a lot actually. Endearingly this was a good thing, as Rex was happy to listen to her banging on and on about something or other. Rex had a thing about voices. A nice voice was enthralling to him, and this young lady made a lovely sound. More than that though, Rex couldn't get over how beautiful Lucy was.

Rex stood just over 6-foot tall, and Lucy was at least five or six-inches shorter than him. She was petite, the perfect size to be wrapped in his arms and cuddled. If it wasn't for the large sticky stain on his T-shirt and paint stripping onion breath, he might have attempted such a suicidal move. Mercifully he didn't and had a stick of mint chewing gum instead. It was a good decision.

As Rex made his way to meet Bradley, a whirlwind of thoughts were running through his mind. His heart was alive in a way he had never known before, inspired by the woman walking at his side.

Finally he realised, if there really was anything as magical as love at first sight...then for Rex Roman - this was it!

Chapter 16 – A Noble Gesture

Saturday 16th November 1974

Bradley was fumbling through his freshly purchased tour programme, unable to focus on any page for more than a few seconds. He was trying to see as much of it as he could as quickly as possible.

'Bradley, this is Lucy,' said Rex, introducing his new and attractive acquaintance.

'Dude, you've hit a home run!' replied Bradley, looking up, seeing the female companion and immediately realising that Rex was punching well above his weight. 'Man, what the heck happened to your T-shirt?' he asked, noticing the stain.

'Lucy accidentally squirted some tomato ketchup on it, so now she's going to buy me a new one.'

'Is she now? You jammy devil!'

As he'd been living in England for seven years, Bradley had picked up a few handy native phrases along the way.

Rex dithered over his selection before finally settling on the design he wanted, which Lucy duly paid for as promised.

'So you like Pink Floyd?' Bradley asked Lucy as he tried to establish her musical credentials.

'I love them. I only have the *Dark Side* and *Meddle* albums, but they're my favourite band by a mile.'

'**One of These Days** was the first Floyd song that Rex ever heard, and I played it to him,' said Bradley, with a sense of pride. He was actually impressed that Lucy had passed the first hurdle of her assessment process.

'Ah yes, the clever use of the delay sound effects on that track is superb.'

'Rex, she's a keeper,' confirmed Bradley, hearing this sterling answer, a winning shot in any game of Nerd Tennis. Tests complete, Lucy had been fully accepted into the gang.

'You here on your own?' Bradley asked, as he began to hatch a plan.

'Yes.'

'Look, why don't you give me your ticket, you can take mine, then you two can sit together and enjoy the show. They're front row seats.'

'Oh, but my ticket...'

'No, I insist. That's what friends are for, right Rex?' suggested Bradley, his mind working overtime assessing the situation. Rex was going to owe him a lifetime supply of Marathon bars for this noble gesture.

Rex just stood in silence as the horse trading concluded in front of him. He changed into his new black T-shirt, admiring the authentic triangular prism design. The fake one, complete with ketchup stain, was thrown into the bin where it belonged.

'Right, take these,' said Bradley, handing Lucy the two tickets. 'Let's all meet up again after the show. This spot works, so let's meet here. We can discuss the gig.'

Lucy handed Bradley her ticket knowing all too well it was one of those 'In the Gods' seats. Bradley would be lucky if he saw the stage, let alone the band. She felt guilty, but Bradley had been very insistent. There was also the matter of the man standing next to her, looking rather dapper in that new T-shirt.

As Rex made his way to the front row seats, he was beaming with pride. He was wearing a brand-new 'official' tour T-shirt that was far superior to the shabby garment he had bought earlier. His stomach was full from the delicious hot dog and ice-light drink. Then, to top it all, he had a beautiful, young woman on his arm. What a day!

Now all Rex had to do was enjoy the show...

* * *

After the show, at the agreed rendezvous point, Bradley, Rex and Lucy were on a post-gig high. Bradley had still enjoyed the spectacle despite his terrible seating position and announced that the lights and projections looked a lot better with a bit of distance.

For Rex and Lucy, given that they had earlier shared their favourite snack together, closely followed by watching their favourite band, Rex was now curious. He was wondering where the next big thing would come from, seeing as things always seemed to happen in 3s.

Being gentlemen, Rex and Bradley insisted on taking Lucy back home. She still lived with her parents, only a couple of miles away from Rex, and she had a midnight curfew in place. All three of them caught the underground and spent the first half of the journey talking about the concert. During the second half, Rex made his move. Rex had read somewhere that if you ask women questions about themselves, they will instantly warm to your caring nature. When he asked Lucy about her interests, he learnt some new things. He found out that she loved: animals, particularly birds, especially budgerigars, her parents and blah, blah, blah…

Now that it was nearly midnight, Maureen Doggitt was peeking through her curtains looking for her daughter. She was surprised when she saw not one, but two figures coming up the path and another one lurking by the front gate.

'Do you think you'd like to go out again next week?' asked Rex as Lucy smiled sweetly on the front step.

'No, I can't. I am…'

'That's okay, I understand.' Rex had already started his slow retreat down the path, saddened by the rejection.

Rex had dated a few girls up to this point in his life but none of them too seriously. Other interests, like hanging out with Bradley or Nan, acting classes and especially Kung Fu tuition meant that a girlfriend always came low on his list of priorities. This time it was different. This girl was special, and Rex knew it straight away.

'No, I'm involved in some pantomime rehearsals with my Dad for the next two weeks. I'm free after that though, and I would love to see you again. How about Sunday the First?'

'Really?' said Rex, rushing back up to the doorstep. This was looking good.

Aha, the third thing in common!

1. Hot dogs.
2. Pink Floyd.
3. Acting. Well, panto - close enough.

Rex couldn't believe his ears and completely forgot to mention that he loved acting, too. That would be something to talk about on the first date.

After swapping phone numbers, Rex lingered on the step wondering what to do...
'***Handshake?*** *Too formal.* ***Cuddle?*** *Bit lame.* ***Kiss on the lips?*** *Too strong.* ***Kiss on the cheek?*** *Yes Rex, that's it! You charmer. You lady killer you. A kiss on the cheek to really knock her socks off. Well played that man!'*

After an awkward moment, Rex kissed Lucy on the cheek so fast that Maureen blinked and missed it. He sped off down the path as swiftly as he could, clumsily knocking over a garden gnome as he left.

'How did it go?' asked Bradley, desperate for the news.

'Sunday the First of December, yours truly has secured a date with Miss Lucy Doggitt.'

'Lucy what???' laughed Bradley.

'Oh yes, didn't you know? Think yourself lucky you weren't drinking a can of coke when I told you that.'

The pair left the scene of triumph and headed towards the nearest underground station, chatting all the way.

On the journey home, Rex recounted the story of the hot dog stand debacle. The ketchup, the T-shirt, and the unique new way of drinking coke all made for interesting conversation. Rex gushed about his feelings as Bradley listened with a sense of pride. Bradley's personal sacrifice of a front row seat, for the greater good of love, was a small price to pay to see the happiness it had brought.

The more Bradley heard, the more he knew Rex had it bad. He'd never seen his best friend quite like this. This was one romance to watch...

Chapter 17 – The First Date

Sunday 1st December 1974

Following on from the Pink Floyd concert, Rex had over two weeks to meticulously prepare for his first date with Lucy. Desperate to ensure that she had an unforgettable experience: he wrote notes, made phone calls, sought advice and finally came up with a winner...

'Two tickets for *Enter the Dragon* please,' said Rex.

Bruce Lee was Rex's hero. Sadly, Bruce had died the year before, but his cult status was alive and well in this classic Seventies Kung Fu flick. Rex was convinced, as he and Lucy had so much in common already, that it was inevitable she would love to go and see the martial arts icon in action.

Other 'date suggestions' were all based around food. Bradley had said that no one could resist the Hard Rock Cafe with its American style burgers and shakes. Nan had recalled how Grandad Bill won her heart with tubs of jellied eels, purchased from the famous Tubby Isaacs stall at the end of Brick Lane. Kate and Roy had suggested a romantic candle-lit meal, but Rex had done the maths and the film looked like a much safer financial bet. Rex also liked very simple food, so he couldn't see the point of an expensive restaurant.

The movie lived up to all expectations and Rex was positively inspired when he came out of the cinema. What a story! ☯ Lee goes to the island fortress of an evil crime-baron, who is staging a brutal martial arts tournament as a cover for his illegal activities. Determined to avenge the death of his sister, Lee is looking to kick some serious butt. Quite frankly, when you have plot lines like these, who needs *Hamlet*?

Lucy was polite about the film, mentioning that the popcorn was good. As they started to walk home, chatting all the way, Lucy held hands with Rex, and he felt on top of the world.

Rex confessed that he wanted to be a professional actor one day. With his Kung Fu skills, now that Bruce was sadly no longer available, maybe he could fill a gap in the market.

Lucy explained that the panto rehearsals in Wimbledon had been fun. Her father was the stand-by Widow Twankey in a stage spectacular of *Aladdin.* Rex responded by saying that he'd always wanted to visit Wimbledon Common. He often wondered if *The Wombles* were based on any real creatures actually living there or whether they were merely a piece of inspired fiction. He was feeling shy and clutching at straws for conversation.

As Lucy continued talking, Rex felt himself falling further under her spell. Lucy had actually grown up in Surrey and therefore had a different, much smoother, accent compared to Rex's North London twang. She had only moved to London in 1969, when she was 14-years-old, on account of her father being promoted at work.

Not wanting the evening to end, Rex offered to take Lucy on a guided tour of the beautiful city they both called home. Rex loved London. He loved the way it looked at night, especially down by the River Thames.

Their arrival at Waterloo signalled the start of a romantic tour with Romeo Rex pointing out that the large four-faced clock, hanging in the middle of the main concourse, was a famous meeting place for lovers. What a smoothie! Lucy snuggled up close to her date, and braving the chilly weather, they made the short trip to Waterloo Bridge in record time.

The amazing thing about Waterloo Bridge is that if you stand in the middle, it offers one of the best viewpoints in London. Rex knew this thanks to The Kinks single, Waterloo Sunset.

As you walk across the bridge, then St. Paul's Cathedral is found to the right. On the left and in the distance, you can see the Houses of Parliament and Rex's favourite structure in the whole of London - Big Ben.

Rex, laying on all of his smooth moves, decided it would be a good idea to walk towards Old Ben. He and Lucy crossed Waterloo Bridge and walked hand in hand along the well-lit Victoria Embankment. They went past Cleopatra's Needle and then stood on Westminster Bridge, gazing at the definitive symbol of the nation's government: The Houses of Parliament.

There was that night, and still is now, something magical about Big Ben. So tall and majestic, the detail in its construction has to be seen to be believed. It is probably the most famous clock in the world, and when you see it standing proud under a bright moon, on a crisp December night, well, such sights are truly unforgettable. *(Most people refer to St. Stephen's Tower as Big Ben. Ben is actually the bell inside the tower. Glad we've cleared that up; you don't have to write in now.)*

From there, they headed off towards The Mall and then onto Buckingham Palace where they stood by the imposing gates, gawping at Her Majesty's humble abode.

NOTE:
We now take a short literary diversion. If you live in London or know London well, then skip the next page. If you don't, then you might find these top tips useful the next time you are on a date in this great capital city.

Rex Roman is not known for his amazing insight into women. He often misses the obvious and is impervious to subtle hints, so the publishers have already discounted the idea of:

The Rex Roman Guide to Romance as a future bestseller.

In truth, it is doubtful that his meagre knowledge could even fill a small pamphlet, an A5 flyer would be more appropriate. Luckily his date with Lucy did make a great impression, thus proving Rex was a superb tour guide at least. Therefore the publishers, always looking to save a few quid, have decided to include a page here to satisfy any future demand for such a *Rex Roman-ce Related* publication:

The Rex Roman Guide to Romance – How to Impress in London

First, ask your date to join you on a romantic tour, starting at Waterloo station. Once on the main concourse, why not point out that the large four-faced clock, hanging in the middle, is a famous meeting place for lovers. With that seed planted, head straight for Waterloo Bridge, it's not that far and it *is* well sign-posted. As you walk on the bridge, over the River Thames, you will see the magnificent St. Paul's Cathedral to your right, and to your left will be the Houses of Parliament. Cross over the bridge, then take the steps on the left down onto the Victoria Embankment. Holding hands as you walk by the river, you will pass Cleopatra's Needle, and then, eventually, you will see the most impressive structure in London - Big Ben. After suitable awe-inspired gazing time, walk along Bridge Street and into Great George Street, keeping Big Ben / Parliament Square to your left. Turn right into Horse Guards Road, keep St. James's Park on your left, then eventually turn left down The Mall. Walk straight ahead, and this will give you the most fantastic view of Buckingham Palace. That's it - the perfect place to end your tour. So, why not put this love encyclopedia to the test. Get out into this beautiful city, take this romantic route and work your magic! If your date fails to be impressed, well... give up and console yourself with a hot dog.

We return to the date...

Eventually the evening had to end, so Rex escorted Lucy safely back home. Maureen had long since given up curtain patrol and gone off to bed.

'I've really enjoyed tonight,' said Rex, standing on the front doorstep, looking at his feet. He was wondering how to ask for another date.

'I have too,' Lucy replied. 'I've been talking about you a lot over the last couple of weeks. I've been really looking forward to this evening.'

'Have you?' Rex was surprised, pleased and bashful all at the same time. He was about to ask for a second date when Lucy saved him from further embarrassment.

'Mum and Dad would like to know if you want to come out with us for an Italian meal, next Saturday night. They would like to meet you. They insist on paying.'

Yes, I would love to,' replied Rex instantly, obviously not thinking straight. Blinded by the offer of a *free* meal and a second date with a goddess, he had completely missed the fact that this meal would involve him meeting Lucy's parents for the first time.

'Great, well come here for six-thirty then.'

'I will. Brilliant! I'll look forward to it...so I'll see you then.' Rex gave Lucy another peck on the cheek before he broke a new world 'path dash' record; he was still a bit shy.

Walking home, Rex had totally lost all track of time. When he finally got in at 3am, Nan woke up, made him a cup of tea and they both sat chatting about the evening's events. There was something different about her grandson, and Nan knew exactly what it was.

Rex was in love. He had a second date, and now all he had to do was make a good impression…

Chapter 18 – Meet the Parents

Saturday 7th December 1974

At some point on Monday the 2nd of December, the implications of meeting Maureen and Peter Doggitt finally sunk in. Rex had realised this wasn't about a *free* meal; this was an interview to see if he was good enough for their daughter.

This potential interrogation gave the second date a whole new twist and added extra tension to the week. On the one hand, Rex couldn't wait to see Lucy again. On the other, he was suffering a crisis of confidence.

Rex did have some positive things going for him. He was decent, honest and his intentions were true, yet he was all too aware that he lived with his Nan, didn't own a car or even really have a proper job. This made Rex panic and worry that he wouldn't be deemed good enough for Lucy, until Nan reassured him that he just had to be himself. Money didn't equal love.

Such wise advice was a welcome comfort, so Rex held tight to his high hopes of a brighter future. Now that Lucy had entered his life, he might just put down the deposit on that tandem bicycle he'd had his eye on after all.

Maybe the sight of Bruce Lee the week before, dispatching an unusually large amount of extras in such a cool manner, made him believe that anything was possible.

Either way, come the 7th of December, Rex Roman was on a mission. He must not fail…

Rex arrived at the Doggitts' at 6.30pm sharp, wearing a fancy new shirt he had bought especially for the date. Nan had pressed the shirt beautifully, and Bradley had given him a squirt of some Old Spice aftershave, just for that killer touch. Rex had it all going on tonight.

'Hello Rex, do come in,' said Maureen as she opened the front door.

'Thank you, Mrs Doggitt,' he replied, nervously crossing the threshold.

The mission had begun!

'Lucy…your date is here,' Maureen shouted up the stairs.

'Rex! I'm so happy to see you,' squealed Lucy, racing down the stairs and planting a big smacker right on Rex's lips, just as a large man entered the hall. 'And this is my Dad, Peter.'

Peter glared, moved forwards and tried to ignore the bright red lipstick stain sat on Rex's top-lip. If Peter was trying to intimidate the new house guest, he was off to a flying start.

'Rex,' said Peter, extending his hand in a business-like manner.

'Hello sir,' replied Rex, acknowledging the gesture and putting his best manly squeeze into the handshake. He wanted to make a strong impression. The combination of an overpowering Old Spice aroma and a lipstick stain on his face meant that Rex was already way ahead in the strong impression department. The 'sir' was a lifesaver.

* * *

A night in a restaurant can be a highly enjoyable social event. Italian food, with its varied menu, can be an excellent choice as everyone can usually find something to eat.

Pasta, particularly penne, *served with pesto sauce, pine nuts, mix in some chicken pieces, then maybe add a light sprinkle of parmesan,* could be described as perfection on a plate. Garlic bread is an optional extra, and if you are on a hot date with a new girlfriend, best avoided at all costs. Rex saw that one coming and dodged it beautifully. The rest he ordered.

Of course, as a group of sophisticated adults enjoying an evening's fine dining, it seemed only natural to have some wine with the meal.

'Another glass of wine, Rex?' asked Peter.

'No thank you, sir,' replied Rex, holding his hand over the top of his empty glass.

During the evening, Rex had begun talking about his love of acting and his job as a part-time martial arts instructor. He also talked about how he met Lucy, and everyone laughed about the whole coke-dribbling-out-of-the-nose drama, much to his relief. Things were going splendidly.

Peter had sat across from Rex, and he seemed to be quite impressed with the young man. His initial wall of reserve had come down, and he made a confession that he too held some thespian ambitions. Peter's own panto career was in the doldrums after a mishap with Captain Hook in 1972, best not discussed over dinner. His real job as the manager of Barclays Bank in Hampstead, held a position of high social status. Rex was surprised to learn that Lucy was a teller at the same branch.

Maureen was just relieved that her daughter had finally found a boyfriend who appeared to be so normal. She may have called Rex by the name of Rick or Graham at least once while Lucy kicked her under the table, but her sometimes forgetful nature only seemed to add to her charm. Rex took a shine to Lucy's parents and started to relax in their company.

It was only when Rex went to the toilet and zigzagged across the room, instead of taking a more natural straight line, that he realised one glass of wine was his limit. Given that he had already consumed two glasses, it was only a matter of time before the wheels fell off his wagon.

The wine had mercifully taken a while to sink in, so plenty of interesting conversation had at least taken place beforehand. Now it was nearing time to leave, Rex was in trouble. Strangely, considering the importance of the date, the trouble didn't seem to concern him that much. His constant giggles and floppy head were very subtle hints to one obvious fact:

Rex was an alcohol lightweight.

* * *

'Cup of coffee, Rex?' asked Maureen as she took her coat off, hanging it up neatly in the hall back home.

'Oh, yes please,' replied Rex, desperate to get to the sofa, willing his legs to carry him the final few steps to safety.

Rex could hear a bout of chuckling in the hallway as he sat his well-oiled frame on the sofa in the lounge. The combination of a spinning room, wobbly head and a total lack of balance prevented him from going outside to see what was so funny.

Before long, Maureen returned with some strong coffee closely followed by Lucy, who held a large plastic bucket in her hands.

'Crikey, you must be thirsty,' said Rex, giggling at his own hilarity as he slapped his thigh in amusement.

'It's for you, sweetheart. Just in case you don't feel well.'

Rex looked hard at the evidence. Earlier, Lucy had rushed down the stairs and planted a big kiss on his lips. Now, she had just called him sweetheart. Things were looking very promising indeed. Rex was playing a blinder.

'Your father and I will be in the other room, dear. We'll give you some space,' said Maureen as she left, closing the door behind her.

'Put your feet up, sweetheart,' instructed Lucy. She could see that Rex was never going to be a hard drinker.

'I don't feel very well.'

'Look, here's a bucket. I want you to lean over, put your fingers down your throat and tickle. You'll feel a lot better.'

Rex desperately wanted to feel better as he was aware of his rapid descent, further and further into alcohol induced oblivion. Groaning, he lent forward over the bucket in order to follow the sensible instructions.

'Tickle what exactly?' asked Rex, not making any progress.

'The back of your throat, behind your tongue.'

As luck would have it, the whole lack of tongue tickling technique didn't matter too much. Almost instantly, Mother Nature's perfect mechanism for self-preservation came noisily to the rescue and solved the crisis. A spot of projectile cleansing ensured the wild man was carrot free and back on the road to recovery.

'I feel better now,' sighed Rex, the relief was immediate.

As Lucy took the bucket outside, Rex could have sworn that he heard howls of laughter just before he fell asleep.

The next morning, a deeply embarrassed and seriously hung-over Rex struck *Beer Taster* and *Wine Expert* from his career list. On the slow shuffle back to Nan's, he decided that it was best to avoid alcohol in the future as he obviously suffered from the *"potentially fatal, allergic condition: Floppy Limbosis"*.

Thankfully, impressed by such a fine performance the night before, Peter and Maureen gave the blossoming relationship their blessing.

Way to go Rex, way to go.

* * *

Chapter 19 – An Englishman Abroad

July 1975

Your first trip abroad is always an exciting time. Your first trip abroad with your girlfriend, is also equally memorable.

Lucy had a grandmother named May. She too was affected by the *"Do you want something to eat, dear?"* epidemic that had swept around London's Nan population. A lovely old lady, she conveniently had a holiday home in France which wasn't used very often. This provided the perfect opportunity for Rex and Lucy to have their first holiday together, with *free* accommodation, as long as they could make the journey.

Lucy had a car. It wasn't much of a car. It was a Fiat 500, which had eye-watering acceleration and a boot the size of a handbag. In truth, the eye-watering part was more often due to tears of frustration caused by a lack of speed, rather than any act of high-performance.

A leaky roof meant that you were in for a really good soaking in wet weather. A non-existent ventilation system ensured either extreme hot or extreme cold conditions on any journey.

There were really only two good things that you could say about the car:

One: It had a wheel at each corner for optimum balance.
(This could count as four things, but we'll say one for arguments sake.)

Two: It had a heart-stopping 498cc sports engine, hence the name - Fiat 500. When this powerhouse of an engine was combined with the wheels, it enabled the car to go faster than Rex on his bicycle…just. 🚲 🚲 🚲

The main advantage of having a car could be summed up in one word. *Freedom!* For all of its faults, and there were many, Lucy's Fiat meant that she and Rex could drive off together anytime they liked. This was exactly what they were about to do.

'Ready?' Lucy asked Rex as she stood on the front doorstep of his home.

'Absolutely! I've packed my phrase book, a few clothes and Nan's baked us some rock cakes.'

To sample one of Nan's rock cakes was an event every dentist would dream of; it kept them in business. Without doubt her bread pudding was legendary, but the rock cakes were always another bad day in the office for Nan. Rex used to wonder if she was baking them just for Roy, so he could bludgeon some poor victim to death with one and then eat the evidence.

Rex was really excited about his first overseas adventure. The destination was France, otherwise referred to as the 'Neighbour from Hell', but he was still keen to go. Monsieur Le Coin had been a great teacher at Winston, so Rex had found French an interesting language to study.

Due to England being invaded by Norman in 1066, a fact Rex learnt in history class, the English language has inherited many of his words. Numerous French words have exactly the same meaning in English, just pronounced with a different accent. A bit of practice and it's easy to make the adjustment.

After a dozen games of I Spy With My Little Eye and several choruses of We're All Going on a Summer Holiday, the journey began to get tedious. Rex jettisoned the rock cakes at the first fuel stop, in case they were slowing the car down with their granite-like weight.

The lack of rocks didn't make too much difference to the car's pitiful speed, and every time Rex asked: 'Are we there yet?' Lucy would reply: 'Just around the corner, sweetheart.'

A reassuring comment until Rex realised there weren't many corners on the newly opened M3 / M27 motorways, running from London to Southampton.

A 4am start to catch the 9am ferry gave the car just enough time to make the trip, with the throbbing power of the engine reaching 50mph on more than one occasion. Lucy was busily commenting on how smoothly the journey had gone when, on arrival at Passport Control, Rex suddenly went as white as a sheet.

'Passports,' asked the officer from within his cabin.

In those days, only the lead passenger had to give their name for the vehicle to embark. On the ticket, that lead passenger was one - Miss Lucy Doggitt.

Rex didn't have a passport in the name of Mr Rex Roman. His passport referred to a name that he had gladly left behind a long time ago. Despite all of Bradley's support, when it came to Her Majesty's Government, Rex didn't officially exist. His photo was there in his passport, but this fugitive, in the front seat of the world's slowest getaway car, had no legal status.

Naturally, Rex had forgotten to mention this small detail to Lucy. He never seemed to find the time or the right moment. With Nan fully supporting the Rex alias, it meant that Lucy didn't suspect a thing.

In front of the car was a barrier, then a series of ramps that led to a docked ferry and a holiday in France, but first they had to get through the formality of showing their passports.

Lucy handed her passport to the official as Rex slumped down further into his seat, hoping he wouldn't be spotted. He sat silently, staring straight forward, waiting for the game to be up. He was about to be found out and exposed. It was all over.

'Passport, sir,' was the request that signalled the runaway's inevitable capture.

Rex had hoped that only Lucy would be required to hand over her papers, but this was not the case. He and Lucy had spent many months planning and saving for their holiday, with Rex preparing countless lists and diagrams. Now he feared they would fall at the final hurdle. Close, but no cigar.

Rex handed over his passport and waited for the fallout...

'That's fine, sir. Have a safe trip.'

That was it. Secret concealed. The path to freedom was clear. Overhead, seagulls hung motionless above the air which indicated a close proximity to the sea, and with the worst part of the journey completed, it was time to board the ferry.

'That went well,' said Rex, feeling thrilled with himself as the Fiat struggled its way up the ramps.

'Why wouldn't it?' asked Lucy, puzzled by Rex's statement.

'Oh, no reason…ooh look, a boat!'

Rex was a master of the diversionary tactic.

* * *

Britain is an island. In 1975, if you wanted to get off of the island, you had two reasonable choices. One way was to fly, the other was to go by boat. *(If you had a fridge full of goose fat, you could also swim. No one would ever be able to dig a tunnel to France big enough to run a train through it. Would they?)*

On a plane you sit in your seat, get bumped by people in front and back, dread going to the toilet and suffer a bout of mild panic the moment you hit any air turbulence.

On a ferry, once you have parked your car, you are free to wander to your heart's content. Rex found this prospect exhilarating, and as soon as the Fiat came to rest, he was eager to explore the large boat.

'Come on, come on,' said Rex, beckoning Lucy out of the car, impatient in his quest to reach the upper decks.

'Calm down, babe. We've got plenty of time before we get to France,' said Lucy. She was so sensible.

Within fifteen minutes and following a full reconnaissance mission, a report was made to Lucy who was reading a book on the top deck. Captain Roman informed his First Mate that he had discovered the Seafarer's Café, which was conveniently located in the same area as the one-armed-bandit gambling machines and the table football.

The intrepid explorers watched from the rear of the ship as dear old Blighty disappeared into the distance. With open sea all around, they jointly decided it was time for some food.

'Full English breakfast and a cup of tea, please,' said Rex as he placed his wooden tray on the metal rails in the café. He slid the tray along the line, making mental notes on which edibles would be worthy of further investigation later on in this epic journey.

As any cardiac surgeon will tell you, the full English breakfast should, by rights, be banned. The Seafarer's Café menu was a recipe for a heart attack, but what a way to go! Bacon, beans, sausages, tomatoes, fried bread and a fried egg. Rex didn't want the egg, but the rest of it was brilliant. The kind lady serving gave him an extra sausage as a very fair exchange for his egg, and this was rapidly shaping up to be the greatest holiday ever.

About thirty-five minutes after his feast, Rex had become well-acquainted with the side of the ship. His breakfast was on an express journey back to shore, and he was feeling decidedly unwell. Choppy waters, combined with the greasy food, didn't seem to agree with this young mariner, and his maiden voyage might not go down as his finest hour.

'That's the worst of it over, honey,' said Lucy as she comforted her railing-hugging hero, trying her best not to laugh. 'I think you should stay up here and get some air.'

Considering the circumstances, this was good advice. The much-hyped 'table football championship' was going to have to wait until another day. Lucy sat on a long bench while Rex lay down beside her and rested his head in her lap.

No matter what time of year it is, on the top deck of a ferry in the English Channel it is always windy. The fresh air did Rex the power of good, as did lying on the bench being gently nursed by Lucy. She stroked his robust mane and continued to read her book, giggling occasionally.

As he lay there, Rex realised that he wasn't really built for a life on the ocean waves and thus, regrettably, crossed *A Life in the Royal Navy*, *Merchant Seaman* and *Pirate* from his dwindling career list.

* * *

In France and disembarked from the ferry, ex-Captain Roman had suitably recovered to begin the task of map reading. Lucy was the driver; Rex was the navigator on the trek to the chateau.

'Ooh look, a Chinese!' pointed Rex as the Fiat trundled slowly into the French town of Rouen. They were nearly there.

'I thought you were reading the road signs,' replied Lucy, far more interested in remembering to drive on the right-hand side of the road.

'Just taking in the local culture, my love,' said Rex, before returning to the task of pretending he could read a map.

Sensibly, Lucy had already obtained excellent directions from her grandmother, and within another ten minutes or so, they arrived at the house.

Set back off the main 'A' road, the holiday home had a bright red front door, blue shutters on the windows and a spacious patio area in the garden. It also had floor tiles throughout, as is often the way in France, and although it was quite spartan inside, for the next week it was home.

It didn't take long to unload the small car, largely due to its very limited carrying capacity. After unpacking, a *"medicinal"* snooze was necessary to help Rex fully recover from his bout of *"food poisoning"* on the ferry.

Rex is fond of the occasional crafty snooze during the day. Science has proved that a thirty minute catnap enhances mental performance. Therefore Rex is not sleeping but *"bravely advancing scientific research"*. He always dresses up a quick kip with some daft excuse about something or other. Naturally no one believes this old guff, but the excuse is still entertaining.

With the scientific research completed, a trip into town for food supplies was planned and executed. Plentiful rations of fresh, local produce were purchased which was convenient as it was nearly time for dinner.

Trying to impress Rex with her domestic skills, Lucy had brought along some classic British food for their first night's meal. She wanted to ensure that they at least had something wholesome to eat as they settled into their new surroundings.

'Fray Bentos pie, baked beans and mash, followed by Angel Delight sound any good?' asked Lucy as Rex lay on the sofa, completing the crossword in the newspaper.

'Brilliant, babe! That sounds great…need a hand?'

'No, you rest. I'll cook tonight. It's your turn tomorrow.'

What a result! But then, Rex had been at death's door on the ship after all.

The Fray Bentos pie was another miracle invention of the time, right up there along with the iconic Party Seven tin. Obviously, the same packaging genius from the Watney's brewery had undertaken some sneaky sub-contracting work for Mr Bentos.

His latest creation was a meat pie, expertly packed into a plate-sized tin. About two-inches deep, containing the finest chunks of beef in rich gravy, this tin had easily cost the man years of his life in research and design. The result was, given an oven, it could be enjoyed anytime for up to three years after its manufacture. How did he do it?

Bringing along a tin of baked beans was a top-drawer move from Lucy. Now simply add the Smash instant mashed potato to enjoy an all-round tasty meal and bring a tear to every tin Martian's eye.

Finally, let's not forget the Angel Delight. How so much fluffy, whipped goodness could be produced from such a small packet, was beyond Rex. Once again another class move from Lucy, the clever little minx.

It was as Rex sat staring at his severely burnt meat pie and equally over-cooked beans, that he heard a muted sniff and then noticed the first tear rolling down Lucy's cheek.

'Thank you, darling,' he said, putting on his bravest face. 'It looks really…er, hmmm…'

Rex was finding it hard to pick exactly the right words.

'Oh honey, it's a disaster,' Lucy sobbed. 'I got the instructions wrong, and I didn't understand the oven, and then I forgot the beans were cooking, and it just, it just…'

'Sweetheart, it's okay. It doesn't matter. You tried your best, and I really appreciate that,' said Rex, comforting Lucy, drying her tears on the sleeve of his shirt.

It takes time and practice to make the perfect instant mash. If you get it wrong…it tastes awful, but if you get it right… it tastes awful! After both daring to try a single mouthful of the white paste slopped on the plates and a few half-hearted prods at the cremated pie, the pair jointly decided that it was time to call it a day. This dinner was a flatliner.

'I think my tummy still hurts a little bit anyway,' said Rex, desperately trying to make Lucy feel better. 'What about some Angel Delight? What flavour did you bring?'

From here things spiralled even further downhill.

Dreams of blackcurrant Angel Delight, lovingly whipped into fluffy peaks, swiftly evaporated as Rex and Lucy stared at the runny purple liquid sitting at the bottom of the mixing bowl. Not a single fluffy peak was in sight.

'I needed a whisk,' whimpered Lucy, on the verge of another bout of tears.

The sight of the distress this whole meal had caused Lucy was too much for Rex to bear. He knew that he had to roll up his sleeves, be a man and rescue the situation for the good of them both.

After all, Lucy was merely trying to cook a hearty meal. She tried her best to make the evening perfect, but so far, it had all gone horribly wrong.

Rex looked at the plentiful supply of fresh, local produce spread out around the kitchen. It was time for a superb meal full of nutritional excess, all prepared with love and attention to detail.

That night, Rex had the best Chinese takeaway he ever had in his life.

* * *

The week went by all too quickly, and having recovered from the 'Fray Bentos incident', things went from strength to strength.

Rex decided that he liked being in France. How can anyone not like being in a country that has over 400 varieties of cheese? This, coupled with the knowledge that Lucy would go weak at the knees whenever Rex said anything in French, only seemed to add to the sense of occasion.

A damsel in distress could be saved by her knight in shining denim with the simple phrase…

"Oú sont les toilettes?"

For this gallant act, Lucy would flutter her eyelashes at an unfathomably fast rate. On seeing this, Rex was glad that he'd studied French, and not German, at school.

No one knows how the car made the journey there and back, but it did, and this was just about the best holiday that anyone could wish for...with the exception of the pie - of course.

SPECIAL OFFER

Rex Roman likes to offer people value for money. As the publishers are deliberately trying to avoid spending any money on graphic artists, to really do any justice to the numerous posters and diagrams in this book, Rex has decided to step in.

Therefore, you will find THREE books for the price of ONE in this publication.

Firstly you have the book itself, surely enough for most people.

Secondly, every budding Lothario's handbook: *(See page 113)*
The Rex Roman Guide to Romance – How to Impress in London

Now, especially for you, we have the third and final title in this book…

The Rex Roman Guide to Handy French Phrases When on Holiday Over There *(The title may need some work)*

French	English
Oú sont les toilettes?	*Where are the toilets?*
Un café-crème s'il vous plaît	*A café-crème (milky coffee) please*
Oui Monsieur	*Yes sir*
Je voudrais un hot-dog	*I would like a hot dog*
Oh la la, le fromage	*Ooh, cheese*
Deux portions de…	*Two portions of…*
Poulet avec des noix de cajou	*Chicken with cashew nuts*
Riz avec des oeufs grillés	*Egg fried rice*
Et des pommes frites	*And chips*
C'est combien, s'il vous plaît?	*How much is that please?*
Merci	*Thank you*
Au revoir	*Bye*
Merci mon Dieu, J'ai faim!	*Thank God, I'm starving!*

Chapter 20 – Raspberry Pastiche

March - May 1976

It was 1.32pm on a wet Wednesday in March 1976, when Nan came home and said she felt a little unwell.

'I knew I shouldn't have had that cucumber sandwich,' said Nan as she stumbled into the lounge. 'It's really sitting on my chest.'

Fortunately, Rex was at home at that precise moment.

Nan looked whiter than usual, and small beads of perspiration had formed on her forehead. She was short of breath and a bit unsteady on her feet.

'Sit down, Nan. Sit down. I'll get you a glass of water.'

As he filled the glass, Rex noticed that his hand was shaking.

Rex had never seen Nan unwell; she always seemed as strong as an ox. Yes, she had a smokers cough; but she'd always had that. Every day started with Nan in the kitchen coughing up a gold watch. Okay, so the house sometimes smelt like an old ashtray, but that was alright. Nan would spray the place with lavender air freshener and open all the windows, the second Rex stepped in through the front door.

Nan slumped into her armchair. Rex handed her the water, stroking her candyfloss white hair to offer some comfort.

'What's wrong, Nan?'

'Well, I was over at Olive's...she made me a lovely sandwich for lunch, but now I don't feel very well. I'll be all right. I just need to catch my breath, that's all.'

Seeing that she was struggling, Rex tipped the glass towards Nan's mouth.

'Where does it hurt, Nan?'

'My chest, it feels like an elephant's sitting on it.'

This didn't sound good…

'Anywhere else?' asked Rex, feeling rather uneasy about these worrying symptoms.

'My left-arm hurts a bit, but it's mainly my chest.'

Rex had heard more than enough. He rushed to the phone, dialled 999 and requested an ambulance, asking if it could be sent immediately to this rapidly growing emergency.

* * *

Everything seemed to be spinning out of control for Rex, and his mind was racing away with panic. He sat with Nan, trying to be positive during the tortuous minutes spent waiting for help to arrive.

When the paramedics placed Nan on a stretcher and into the back of an ambulance, Rex found the sight distressing. Seeing the oxygen mask on her face only seemed to add to the gravity of the situation. One paramedic held her hand while the other radioed on ahead to the hospital.

Rex called Lucy at work. She tried her best to reassure him, but the phone call was brief. He was too concerned to talk. He just wanted to let her know what had happened.

The next call was to Bradley, to try and arrange a lift to the hospital as soon as possible. Rex had decided to remain at home to collect some personal items for Nan. It looked like she might be away for some time; she was in a bad way.

A small crowd of people had gathered outside the house. They had obviously heard the ambulance siren or maybe seen its flashing lights and were curious about what was happening.

'What's going on?' said one kid as he pulled up on his bright red Chopper push bike.

'Some old lady got put in the back of the ambulance,' replied someone else.

Rex didn't need to know who had said these cold words in such a non-caring manner, but the truth cut like a knife.

That old lady was his beloved Nan, his 74-year-old lifelong friend who seemed to be an ageless classic. For the first time in his life, Rex realised she did actually look like an old lady now.

* * *

When Rex arrived at the hospital, the doctor confirmed the paramedic's diagnosis - Nan had suffered a heart attack.

Rex was shown through to a ward full of the elderly, all in need of special care, every one of them hopefully treasured as much as Nan. Using an oxygen mask to breathe, with a drip in her arm, Nan was unconscious and free from pain. Rex sat by her bedside for several hours, relieved that she was still alive and praying for her recovery.

'She'll be all right,' said a nurse as she came to check on her patient.

Rex looked up, made a weak attempt at a smile and sighed.

'Why don't you go home and get some rest, love. You look tired. We'll take good care of her. All she's going to do is sleep. Come see her tomorrow.'

Rex was tired. The stress of the whole situation was making him feel exhausted. The nurse was right; it was a much better idea to go home for a while and get some rest.

Outside the ward, Bradley had sat all by himself, waiting for news. He didn't want to intrude in case Nan had taken a turn for the worse. For over three hours, he had just waited and waited with nothing to do. He didn't complain once.

* * *

Within a couple of days, Nan was off the oxygen and eating very small amounts of food. After a week, she was able to sit upright in bed.

'Hello my darling,' said Rex as he arrived at the bedside. He knew this traditional daily greeting would be well-received.

'Ooh hello,' replied Nan, her eyes lighting up.

'How are you feeling today? When are you coming home?'

'I don't know. They keep prodding me with needles and taking blood. I'm getting fed up with it.'

Rex offered some reassuring words...

'They're just taking good care of you, Nan. As soon as you're ready, I'll take care of you at home.'

'You're such a good boy,' said Nan, thrilled at the prospect.

Rex went to see the doctor to find out when Nan would be leaving. He wasn't prepared for what he heard…

'We've found a shadow on her lung. We need to do some more tests, so I'm afraid she won't be coming home just yet.'

'Shadow on her lung?' Rex began to panic. The implications of this were terrifying, yet he just didn't want to imagine the worst. Not now, not ever.

Thinking back, Rex realised that Nan hadn't seemed herself for quite some time. If Nan was ill though, she would never complain, she just got on with it. In her day a broken leg was something you walked off. Having lived in London through two World Wars, this was one tough old bird.

Another month went by, and every day Rex went to the hospital. One day, Nan had mentioned that she thought the lounge wallpaper was looking a bit dirty, so she wanted to change the colour. The next day, Rex took in a paint colour-chart, and for whatever reason, Nan picked out raspberry.

Rex scheduled his life around visiting hours at the hospital and painting the lounge in the new fruit-based theme. He did a really meticulous job too, making sure everything was perfect for when Nan came home.

* * *

It was just before 3pm on Sunday the 9th of May 1976, when Rex arrived at the hospital.

Nan was asleep and looking frail. Rex sat holding her hand as he had done every day for the past six weeks. He was quietly reading the newspaper, waiting for some signs of life when suddenly, Nan squeezed his palm in a vice-like grip.

'Is that you, Rex?' Nan mumbled. She was in a semi-conscious state, her head slumped to one side.

'I'm here, Nan.'

'I love you, Rex.'

Nan never said this. Rex had told his Nan that he loved her on numerous occasions. He'd grown up telling her so; there was no shame in it. Nan meant the world to him, but *she* just didn't show this sort of emotion. It wasn't her way. Nan's love was expressed through a lifetime of actions.

'I love you, Nan,' said Rex as tears rolled down his cheeks.

Nan died at 4.53pm.
She never did wake up nor say another word.

* * *

The funeral was a lovely service, everybody said so. Kate comforted Rex throughout, and even Big Roy gave him a hug. Bradley shed a few tears for his adopted grandmother, and Lucy didn't know what to say, she wished she'd known Nan a lot longer.

Olive was there, shocked at losing her best friend and probably feeling her own mortality, she seemed overcome by the day.

Anna turned up out of respect for her grandmother. The latest news was that Sandra had left Ray, and she was now married to someone else. He was a good man this time; she was finally happy but still as nutty as a squirrel's breakfast. No one knew where Ray was; but then again, nobody cared. Rex shared a cuddle with his sister and they promised to make a better effort to keep in touch, now that she was no longer living at home.

Outside, after the cremation, the sun was shining down on the memorial courtyard. A framed picture of Nan, smiling as she sat in her garden, rested on an easel. Beneath it were the flowers that so many friends had kindly brought to honour the memory of this special woman.

Rex looked at his own floral tribute, beautifully crafted into three simple letters.

NAN

Goodbye my darling
x

A page for quiet contemplation before we resume…

Chapter 21 – Dingo Dawson

Thursday 24th June 1976

The weeks and months following Nan's death were really tough for Rex, and he had many sleepless nights.

Nan had left Rex everything in her will. Fortunately for him, that included the house which she and her husband Bill had bought, and paid for, many years ago. Nan wanted Rex to stay in the family home. Her two sons were both happily married and comfortable, so Nan felt that Rex was the one that would need taking care of. Everyone was happy with the arrangement.

To occupy his mind, Rex set about re-painting the lounge from the fresh new raspberry pastiche to a far more calming blue. Now that he had so much time on his hands, he decided to paint the walls dark blue at the bottom, pale blue at the top, and put a yellowy decorative paper border across the middle. He liked it that way. When Rex finished the lounge, he painted the hall, then the bedrooms and so on... until he'd been through the whole house and there was nothing more to do.

All of Nan's clothes were donated to the local charity shop. During the packing, Rex could vividly picture her wearing each garment. Due to overwhelming emotions, it took several days to complete this sad task. He would frequently expect Nan to come in through the door, gasping for a cup of tea. She never did.

While clearing a cupboard, Rex found nearly £1000 stuffed inside an old jam jar. The canny old lady had saved it for a rainy day. He also found the legendary bread pudding recipe, which was a great source of comfort.

Rex tried to give all the money to his uncle and absent father, but they insisted on splitting it between the 'three' sons that Nan loved so much. Rex and his father started to talk more as they both shared a common grief, and so their awkward relationship began to improve after some years of distance. Nan would have thoroughly approved.

As for the Milwee family, they did everything they could to support Rex. They gave him the necessary time and space to come to terms with his loss. The same was true of Lucy. If Rex rang in tears, she would listen. If he wanted her company, she would drive over. When Rex came out the other side of his despair, Lucy was standing there with open arms ready to hold him. Their bond became stronger through the whole, heart-breaking experience.

When Steve Brown paid a home visit, Rex saw another side to the fearsome fighter. Steve was full of Chinese wisdom about life and death, based on the teachings of the great philosopher - **Confucius**. The rationale imparted over a cup of tea, gave Rex a real sense of peace and an even deeper respect for his teacher.

Eventually, Rex scheduled a return to his acting classes and confirmed a desire to maintain his role in a play, destined to open at the Richmond Theatre. A phone call to the outside world was his first tentative step back, after weeks of self-imposed isolation at home. It is often said that to really understand your art, you have to suffer for it. Rex had emotionally suffered, and now his acting would have more depth to it, with added grit in his soul and a source of pain in his heart.

In some ways, Nan's death moved Rex forward. He had always enjoyed her company, yet he knew that nothing could last forever; such is the way of life. He had just wanted to savour every moment with Nan, for as long he could.

* * *

The summer of 1976, was a scorcher. It was the first time that many had known such prolonged high temperatures, and the whole country was on a water alert, due to a severe drought.

Rex knew that he had to start spending time with friends and end his reclusive mourning. Bradley's big gig, at London's famous Marquee Club, would provide a perfect opportunity to rejoin the world.

Bradley was the lead guitar player in Tiger Bay. He got the idea for the name after seeing the James Bond film *Goldfinger.* The film's theme tune had been sung by Shirley Bassey who was an international star and also heralded from a place in Wales called - Tiger Bay. Bradley thought this was inspired.

If the band's name was inspirational then their manager was not. His name was Derek Dawson, but on account of him coming from Australia, everyone called him - 'Dingo'.

Dingo Dawson was a real loud-mouthed-know-it-all and a disgrace to the Australian nation. An 'outback Aussie', it was often said, the sole reason he wasn't wearing a hat with corks on was because they couldn't make one big enough to fit his head. Dingo was so short that even his platform boots still left him vertically challenged. He only ever dressed in black and had long, straggly hair which was obviously thinning. 'Handsome' was definitely not the first word that sprang to mind when you saw him.

Bradley didn't really like Dingo that much. Yet, as he was full of talk about what he was going to do for the band and how they were going to be huge stars, Bradley suffered him. Foolishly, the rest of the guys in the band thought Dingo was the best chance they had; they all desperately wanted to be successful and famous.

As Rex had been spending more time with Lucy over the last couple of years, Bradley had been working towards his dream. He practised hard, attended rehearsals, played various pub gigs and even made some demo recordings of the Tiger Bay anthems. These demos had been heard by a few A&R people from various record labels, so the Marquee gig was more of a showcase. Things were all moving in the right direction.

For Charlie, the illustrious owner of the Record Box, things weren't so good. A combination of factors, namely the bleak national economy, the run-down shop's poor location and his own disgraceful personal hygiene, probably all contributed to the Box folding. Only a few weeks earlier, as Charlie closed the shop door, the bell went ding-a-ling for the last time.

Charlie had started a brand-new career. This one required no costly premises, and it was well-suited to his lifestyle choice of avoiding soap and water. ***He became a roadie!***

For Charlie, being a gear-shifting-gorilla was not good enough. He had ambition. He wanted to be a technician; maybe even one day, he would be a sound engineer. Everyone needs a dream, if not a deodorant. Starting at the beginning, he had learnt the model number of every microphone currently on the market. Charlie was a Nerd Tennis champion, so he took to learning obscure details about equipment with zeal and great passion, collecting them in his brain, ready to serve at any opportunity.

Rex and Lucy had arrived at the Marquee Club to witness the sound check. Dingo was strutting around like a peacock, with Charlie waddling behind in his shadow as the dynamic duo began to set up Tiger Bay's equipment. Lucy had to avert her gaze in horror when Charlie bent over a large wooden box and started rummaging around inside. His jeans were hanging low, and he fully exposed the dark side of his moon.

'Charlie! Get me a 57,' yelled Dingo.

'Don't you want a 58 instead?' Charlie asked.

'Nah, mate. The 57's the go.'

'Is the 58 not a more robust capsule then, Dingo?'

'NO! I want a 57.'

'I think you'll find that even though the 57 and 58 both share the same cartridge, the 58 has a superior pop filter for vocals.'

'CHARLIE! Just get me a f*@#!^g 57, will ya?'

Rex was bewildered by this argument over numbers. The mystery was solved when Charlie emerged from his frantic search with a microphone in his hand. It was when, a few minutes later, Charlie started speaking into the 57, that things got even more confusing...

'Icicles, tricycles, bicycles.'

'Yeah, yeah. Keep going, mate.'

'Icicles, tricycles, bicycles... icicles, tricycles, bicycles.'

'Yeah, mate…nice one, Charlie. Just wait there a minute.'

Acting on Dingo's instructions, Charlie was sound checking the 57 on stage while Dingo was behind a large sound-desk, annoying the in-house engineer. Dingo's big mouth and cocky attitude didn't naturally endear him to many people. His monotonous mantra of: *"Look mate, I've been doing this for fourteen years,"* probably didn't help. He wouldn't listen to any advice from the Marquee's sound engineer, and Bradley could see that trouble was brewing.

A more traditional microphone testing procedure, used the world over to this current day, is…

'One, two…one, two…one, two.'

Obviously, anyone within earshot who is not from the musical brotherhood will immediately respond with the hilarious…

'Three, four…three, four…three, four.'

There can't be a musician on earth that ever tires of hearing that chestnut of a gag - ever!

Dingo's revolutionary, new Southern Hemisphere phrase for testing the frequency range of a Shure SM57 microphone, robbed Rex of a golden chance to impress Lucy with his own ingenious: *"one, two…three, four,"* quip.

The sound check went on and on and soon became tedious, so Lucy and Rex left the venue. They had arranged to meet Bradley in Leicester Square at 7pm, before the show, where they could all relax and have something to eat.

* * *

Bradley was nervous about the gig, so he wasn't very hungry, but he went along to Leicester Square anyway, once the sound check was complete. Rex found his appetite for both food and life were returning. Charged by the buzz of London, he was glad to be out of the house with his two favourite people.

'How's it going then, Bradley? The venue is brilliant,' said Rex, trying to encourage his friend as they sat in a suitable eatery.

'Man, that Dingo, he's an idiot, he really is. We were doing a sound check, and he was shouting instructions at the sound engineer, just barking at him like a dog. The engineer didn't look very happy.'

'I thought he did lights, not sound,' said Rex, puzzled again.

'He thinks he can do everything,' replied Bradley, rolling his eyes to the ceiling.

'Why doesn't he just stick to one thing?' questioned Lucy, as sensible as ever.

'He can't help himself. He did some small-time show in Brisbane once, and now he thinks he **is** the music business. He drives me mad.' Bradley was clearly frustrated.

Over the next hour, the three friends chatted, shared some food and gradually, Bradley felt better. This was after all a huge opportunity tonight, and he just wanted to enjoy it, no matter what.

The Marquee Club has seen many of the all-time greats play on its stage. Jimi Hendrix, Eric Clapton and even Pink Floyd have all played there on their way to the top. A gig at this prestigious venue was considered an important stepping-stone on the path to success.

Aah, the world of the musician. Glamour, fame, money, non-stop fun all the way, with a licence to travel the world like a Viking warrior, enjoying your spoils wherever you lay your guitar case. One hit album and the whole world falls at your feet, chanting your name everywhere you go. Well that's what it seems like to anyone on the outside looking in, right?

On the inside looking out, it's slightly different…

'Mind your feet,' said Bradley, like a gentleman, as Lucy and Rex wandered through the backstage area. 'It's a bit wet back here, I'm afraid.'

For all of its glamour, the toilets backstage at the Marquee Club had serious problems with their plumbing. Ask any musician who has ever played there. They will confirm this fact. The dressing rooms were really small, and every band passing through felt compelled to sign their names, in black marker, on the white walls. A few musicians had even contributed chewing gum, presumably so their DNA could be extracted by future advances in medical cloning, thus hopefully ensuring their own immortality.

To a beautiful young woman like Lucy, used to the more pristine conditions of Barclays Bank in Hampstead, it was a bit of a shock.

At 10pm it was showtime, so Rex and Lucy took their viewing positions at the back of the venue, standing next to the sound desk. They were genuinely looking forward to the gig when suddenly, they witnessed an unfortunate turn of events.

Dingo had barked some instructions to the sound engineer who, by this time, was totally fed-up.

'You know what, mate. You do it!' spat the engineer, walking away from the sound-desk just as the titans of rock, Tiger Bay, burst onto the stage.

'No worries,' said the confidently deluded Dingo.

The assembled crowd of 31 people, clapped enthusiastically in anticipation of a stellar performance. Roy whipped the audience into frenzy with a true American style 'Whoa, yeah!', and the band played on…

Unless you are an octopus, you are going to find it very difficult to operate a sound mixing desk and a lighting desk simultaneously. After this gig, Roy was probably going to help Dingo return to the sea, but the overly optimistic Antipodean pygmy was definitely no octopus.

Lucy pointed out that Dingo was wearing more foundation and eye-liner than she was. Sadly, the time that Dingo had spent applying his make-up should have been spent reading the equipment manuals. He was absolutely hopeless.

Large parts of the set were in almost complete darkness. All of Bradley's guitar solos would start, only for a spotlight to shine on him just as he finished. The drums sounded awful, and the lead singer's microphone kept feeding back. No one knew if the bass player was even plugged in. It all made the panto at Wimbledon look very professional indeed. Some forty-seven minutes later, it was over.

The extreme heat of the summer night had made the walls sweat in the venue, it was that hot. Dingo had failed to use waterproof mascara and many in the small crowd thought he was an Alice Cooper look-alike.

Rex and Lucy felt a range of emotions about the performance:

Relief it had finished. They had no cushions to cover their faces as they watched the horrors unfold.

Concern about how they were going to tell Bradley just how awful the show was. Best leave that one to Kate and Roy.

Anger that this bizarre little man, masquerading as a sound engineer, could possibly think that he had any talent.

Dingo was on an ego trip and Bradley's dreams had just been crushed on the journey. In truth, the brash Aussie was totally out of his depth, and in pursuit of his own personal glory had ruined Bradley's big gig. Charlie was sat humming backstage, bewildered by the awful sound he'd just heard; he had some studying to do later. Charlie had the true scent of a roadie but none of the skills. It was early days yet.

The record companies were terribly polite.

'*Punk rock* is the new sound,' they said, 'your sound is old now.'

Bradley had talent and was undoubtedly a great guitarist, but punk rock was all about *not* being able to play. Attending a punk concert often meant sticking safety pins in your clothes, ears or nose and utilising a rather unpleasant disposal method for your excess saliva, while jumping up and down in a pogo-like motion. Punk was all about attitude. In 1976, it was **the** anti-establishment movement sweeping the musical landscape. Whatever it was, it wasn't for Bradley.

Tiger Bay lost a lot of heart after the gig and fell apart a few months later. On the London circuit, Dingo became rightly known as the 'Blunder from Down Under' and very quickly disappeared. Rumour has it that he went back to Brisbane, boasting of how successful he had been over in England.

Rex didn't believe this. He strongly suspected that Roy had been hard at work again. Good!

Chapter 22 – Rex Is Back!

Wed 21st - Sun 24th July 1976

This Week Only. On Sale Now.

A Brother's Love

Starring Guy Paris & Rex Roman

Co-starring:

Sam Michaels, Gary Summers & Eva Cullen

& Introducing Fly the wonder dog

Written, produced and directed by

Gordon Campbell

Wed 21st – Sat 24th July. 8pm. Tickets £5

The poster outside the Richmond Theatre told the world and the residents of Richmond, that Rex Roman was back!!! A reasonable sized venue, this theatre was responsible for many innovative 'off West End' productions. Tonight, saw the first show in a four night run of an experimental play. The names in chalk, on the fold-up board outside the theatre, let the world know exactly who was performing.

All the big names were there that opening Wednesday night: Roy, Kate, Bradley, Lucy, Peter and as it was a special occasion, Maureen wore her best fluffy jumper. Even the mighty Neville came along to offer some moral support.

Rex was happy to be playing the supporting role to a vastly more experienced Guy Paris. This fine actor was insistent that Rex should be allowed to retain his place in the cast even though, following the sad passing of his Nan, he had missed many of the early rehearsals.

Rex and Guy had been cast as two brothers by one of the trustees of the theatre - Mr Gordon Campbell.

The synopsis found on the official programme read like this:

Two Brothers. One Unbreakable Bond.

When Edward *(Roman)* discovers his brother Eric *(Paris)* has been injured in a freak accident, his world falls apart. Told to prepare for the worst, Edward refuses to give up hope. This touching story, of compelling drama, will move you to both tears of sadness and joy.

* * *

Approaching the end of the play, when Eric slipped into an unconscious state, only to be revived later, Rex was supposed to utter the heart wrenching and imaginative line:

'Eric - don't leave me!'

However, things didn't quite go according to plan.

After an uncomfortable, overly extended silence, it soon became clear that Rex had frozen. The emotion of the scene had triggered painful memories of those final moments at Nan's bedside.

On the positive side, this meant that his performance had some extra raw emotion; Rex could identify with his character. On the negative side, as a few of the audience coughed and spluttered during the lengthy silence, Rex had completely lost where he was.

The immortal line that followed could be the title of many an actor's autobiography:

'SHIT! I've completely forgotten my line'

On hearing this, 364 people in the Richmond Theatre simultaneously burst into hysterical laughter, including the supposedly comatose Eric lying in the bed on stage…oh, and the rest of the cast. Lucy couldn't breathe for laughing, Roy was wiping away tears from behind his dark glasses and Maureen was busily nudging Peter. It was the only laugh of the night. With the whole theatre in uproar, there was just *one* person left not laughing - Gordon Campbell. Standing stage-right with a copy of the script in his hand, the immortal line was definitely ***not*** in it.

Deciding he was totally busted, Rex decided to milk it for all it was worth. He stood up, smiled and then bowed to the audience. Some members rose to their feet, clapping wildly, so Rex added the thespian wave to the next bow. The more they clapped, the more he hammed it up. *'What's the point of taking it too seriously,'* he thought. Rex liked the sound of both the applause and the laughter. He was going to milk it further, until Eric sat upright in his sick bed and threw a banana at him for over-acting. It took a good few minutes for the raucous crowd to settle down in their seats so that the play could come to its conclusion.

A few titters continued to ripple around the theatre for the remaining scenes. You could say there weren't many dry eyes in the house, yet none of these were for the same reasons as Gordon Campbell had envisaged.

Rex was mobbed at the merchandise stand during the 'meet and greet' after the show. It felt good, signing his name on the programmes and sharing a joke with the public. He stood chatting to anyone that came along and didn't return to the dressing room for nearly forty-five minutes.

Back in the dressing room, everyone was still buzzing from the rapturous, final standing ovation. Even Gordon got to see the funny side...eventually.

The next day, word spread around Richmond and beyond. As a result, ticket sales were up for the evening's 8pm show. It was the same story on Friday and amazingly, for the final Saturday night, there was a full house of over 800 people. Much to his relief, Rex turned in a faultless performance every night, remembering all of his lines. After the show, Rex would go out and chat with members of the audience, signing programmes at the merchandise stand. He was happy to take their photos for them as they posed with the remarkable Guy Paris.

Gordon, probably inspired by the box office takings, totally forgave Rex for his theatrical improvisation and promised it would not hinder his future career. Coincidentally, Gordon's next masterpiece was a comedy which would open in the New Year. Rex would be perfect for the lead in this play, so he gladly accepted the role.

Gordon had seen an audience respond far better to comedy than they did a dark, serious piece of theatre. In an ironic way, Rex had saved both Gordon and himself with his virtuoso, ham performance. Nan would have loved it.

Bradley was inspired by the way Rex had turned a potential disaster into a triumph. Such inspiration gave Bradley a real reason to carry on in the arts. He promptly cancelled any plans to sell his guitar, following the Marquee gig fiasco, as he had seen that with the right frame of mind, a victory can always be snatched from the jaws of defeat.

After the opening Wednesday night of *A Brother's Love*, in a heightened state of euphoria, Rex had suggested to Lucy that she should move in with him *one day*. By 6pm on the Sunday, she was cooking a roast chicken dinner in the kitchen, her clothes neatly hung in the bedroom wardrobe, her toiletries strewn throughout the bathroom. Rex had a brief grumble about the mess and wondered if Lucy moving in was a bad idea, until he tasted the crispy roast potatoes and decided it was good to have some company after all. By the time they both settled down to watch television that night, Lucy had already become an indispensable part of life at chez Roman. Harmony at home would provide a bedrock for Rex now that he had taken his first steps into the professional world of acting.

Little did Rex know, events were now set in motion that would bring about even more incredible chapters in his life...

Chapter 23 – Lucy Moves In

Sunday 25th July 1976 & The First Week

In a completely amateur move, Rex forgot to establish the ground rules for Lucy moving in. Such was his joy following the opening performance of *A Brother's Love* that he didn't write up a single list. Therefore, he wasn't at all prepared for the arrival of Stanley.

Stanley was Lucy's budgie. Rex had always assumed he was the Doggitt household family pet, but in fact sole ownership of Stanley belonged to Lucy. She even had the certificate to prove it.

Stanley was an attractive green budgerigar with a long tail and a cute yellow patch on his chest, which looked like a vest. Lucy had named him in memory of her grandfather who often wore a vest, although one made of string not feathers. Stanley's favourite expression was *"What you doing?"*, and his hobbies included watching television, eating trill and ringing his bell.

To add some feminine charm to her new home, Lucy also brought a rubber plant, several ornaments, some furniture, her extensive record collection, lots of clothes and more shoes than Rex thought it was possible for any one woman to own.

Rex knew that Lucy's Fiat 500 could not carry much, so he felt falsely confident about the whole moving in thing. He had totally forgotten about Peter Doggitt's Volvo estate. A car so spacious, with its fold down seats and handy roof rack, that Rex thought it was the automobile version of a magician's hat. Stuff just kept on coming out of it.

Rex had a bit of a huff and a puff about Stanley until Lucy made some promises. First, she pledged that every Sunday there would be a full roast dinner, with all the trimmings, as rent for the new tenant. Then, to further sweeten the deal, she promised Rex that he never had to clean the cage or do any Stanley related chores.

'His chirping will put me off learning my lines,' whined Rex.

'Put him in the bedroom, cover him over and he'll sleep,' replied Lucy.

'He'll ring his bell when *The Sweeney* is on. He'll know it's my favourite programme.'

'He can watch it with us on the sofa instead.'

Lucy had an answer for everything.

Stanley had a clever party-trick up his wing. Whenever Lucy let him out of his cage, he would immediately fly around the room in a mad dash, stretching his wings in excitement. After a five minute flurry, he would settle down onto Lucy's shoulder and sit there for hours, watching television, until she gently carried him back to his cage, perched on her index finger. You had to be there.

That Monday evening, Rex watched the whole of *The Sweeney* with Stanley on his shoulder.

'I love this bird!' gushed Rex as Detective Inspector Jack Regan taught another East End gangster who was the Guv'nor.

Lucy shook her head and laughed. She loved her boys.

During the first week, living with Lucy went fairly smoothly. On Tuesday and Wednesday, Rex discovered that Lucy would always like a cup of tea when she got home from work. Too tired to speak, she would just look at him with puppy dog eyes and make a 'T' sign with her two index fingers. It was the cutest way to order a cuppa, so Rex always made the tea. On Thursday, Rex went training with Neville and the gang.

On Friday, Lucy discovered Rex's secret shame.

For some bizarre reason, never fully understood by Rex, he had a fascination with looking at the fish-counter in the local supermarket. He was in awe of how many varieties of fish there were and how well-presented the display was. As if the heaps of crushed ice, wedges of fresh lemon and dead fish weren't enough, sprigs of parsley made for a classy finishing touch. It was all essential viewing on any shopping trip.

Rex thinks his obsession stems back to his childhood when Grandad Bill used to take him to Billingsgate Fish Market, in London, to buy fresh food for the family dinner. The market traders used to throw the fish back and forth over the heads of the gathered crowd as deals were struck, and the gasping audience clapped. It was a really entertaining spectacle, like a piece of theatre involving dead sealife. It was very sad that the fish were dead. Rex would never kill any living creature, but a man must eat and fish *are* part of the food chain...
best battered, served with chips and covered in ketchup.

Over the weekend, Rex realised that Lucy was his perfect live-in companion for the following reason...

As we have mentioned earlier, Rex took huge artistic inspiration from Steve Austin, *The Six Million Dollar Man*. Rex was therefore thrilled when Lucy revealed her top secret identity. She was Jaime Sommers, aka *The Bionic Woman*.

As Rex and Lucy were adjusting to a new life living together, if they felt any tension, they would swiftly resolve the issue with a good fight. In truth, this was not your ordinary fight. No way. If you have a man worth six million dollars battling a woman worth seven million *(you've got to allow for a bit of inflation)*, then you have 13 million dollars worth of raw power having a ding-dong in North London, just for fun.

Reassuringly, the U.S. government didn't have to worry too much about its bionic investment. This is because all of the fights were conducted in super slow-motion, with tongues firmly planted in cheeks.

Rituals began with Lucy deliberately provoking Rex into a mock fury, which would then result in a tense stand-off. As Rex moved forward with a punch at 0.1mph, Lucy, with her amplified hearing, greatly strengthened right-arm and enhanced legs, was more than a match for the eagle-eyed former astronaut. She would sidestep the punch, then unleash her power with a counter-strike to the jaw. Rex would pull all the correct facial expressions of a man taking a killer blow and fall over in a dramatic fashion - *Slowly*. He was so happy that Lucy was game for a laugh. Now that she was living in Rex World, it was essential that nothing was taken too seriously.

(For anyone old enough to remember these two bionic heroes, from the hugely popular Seventies television series, you will realise that Rex and Lucy were indulging in nothing more than a piece of harmless role-play. If you missed the shows, why not Google them and have a look. This was proper television!)

So that was the first week. It all went pretty smoothly really. With Lucy around, Rex felt so much more determined to forge ahead with his career plans. He wanted to make his girlfriend proud and provide for their future.

The following Monday at 8.30pm, Rex was getting ready for the 9pm showing of *The Sweeney* on ITV. Tonight, in another classic episode, a bank raid was going to go horribly wrong and London's special police unit, The Flying Squad, would be called in. Carter (Dennis Waterman) and Regan (John Thaw) were going to shout: ***"Shut It!!!"*** with alarming frequency, while solving the crime, recovering the cash and roughing up a few villains or *"slags"* along the way. Eventually, near the end of the show, the tough no-nonsense copper, D.I. Regan, would shout: ***"You're Nicked!!!"***. All of that pretty well made for a perfect evening in. Rex couldn't wait.

Suddenly, the phone rang…

'Honey, can you get that, it'll be Mum. I just remembered I asked her to ring at eight-thirty to discuss Dad's birthday arrangements,' Lucy shouted from the bathroom. 'Tell her I'm washing my hair...I've got shampoo in my eyes...keep her entertained for five minutes, she likes talking to you.'

'Okay, sweetheart. I think I can manage that,' said Rex, already mentally preparing his next comedic stand-up routine.

As he picked up the phone, knowing it was Maureen, Rex said something that he wished he hadn't…

'Rex Roman International Superstar. How can I help you?'

Rex thought this greeting was hilarious and was trying not to laugh as he finished his deluded one-liner.

'Well, I do like an actor with confidence,' said a voice, way too deep to be Maureen's.

Rex blushed a wonderful shade of pillar box red and quickly began to backtrack...

'I am so sorry. I thought it was my girlfriend's mother. I am so embarrassed, I really do apologise…'

'Relax, relax,' said the mystery caller. 'Rex, my name is Crispin Hansen. I saw your performance in Richmond the other week.'

'Which night?' asked Rex with some trepidation, missing the point that a complete stranger knew his name and had somehow obtained his home telephone number.

'Saturday night, I thought you were very good.'

That was a relief. Saturday was a full house and by far the best show.

'Rex, I'm a professional agent, I think we should talk. Would you like to come to my office?'

This was a dream come true. This was everything that Rex had been wishing for since he'd left school, even before that.

'I would love to, sir,' confirmed Rex, full of excitement.

'Good. Come along tomorrow at noon. Number Fourteen, Hanover Square. Don't be late.'

The phone went dead, and so did Rex. Dead quiet. First came the shock, and then came Lucy, with a towel wrapped around her head.

'What's wrong, honey? Is Mum okay?'

'It wasn't Mum. It was an agent.'

'An agent? What did he say?'

Lucy was far more excited than the traumatised ex-comedian.

'He wants me to go his office tomorrow at noon. I've heard of this guy. He's actually a proper agent. He's well-known. I can't believe it.'

Lucy put her arms around Rex and gave him a huge cuddle. Armed with an emergency pot of tea and an overflowing biscuit tin, they sat and they talked for hours about what this unexpected phone call could possibly mean for their future. Rex never did find out how the car-chasing, thug-thumping, bank raid case was successfully solved on *The Sweeney* that night. In frustration, Stanley rang his bell - a lot!

Chapter 24 – Rex Meets Crispin

Tuesday 3rd August 1976

Hanover Square is one of the more upmarket business addresses in London. Centrally located, the nearest tube is Oxford Circus. The Oxford St West/Regent St South exit (no.3) is the best way out from the underground station, and then turn left once you are up the stairs. Now on Regent Street (Look for a sign showing *Nos 1-259* high up on the corner wall) take a short walk south. Next, take the first right-turn into Princes Street, walk straight ahead, and within seconds you are in Hanover Square.

Once you are there, you cannot fail to be impressed by the splendour of the buildings and the well-maintained shrubbery in the middle of the square.

If you are Rex Roman, you can arrive twenty-five minutes early, anxiously pace around the area and gradually build yourself up into a state of panic about a potentially life-changing meeting.

If you are not, then simply enjoy the flowers instead.

* * *

Sitting in the reception area of CH Entertainments, Rex found the experience especially daunting. The walls were covered with photos of Crispin and various leading lights from the world of showbiz. *'Handsome devil'* Crispin was too, much younger than Rex had expected, probably only in his early thirties. With a warm beaming smile, good teeth, luxurious hair and chiselled features, he certainly had film star looks. The impressive size of his shirt collars gave clear indication this was a man at the top of his game.

Next to a bookcase, four giants of British television were immortalised in framed photos. One had signed his photo with 'Crispin you're the best', and the other three had signed their own glowing tributes. (*Due to legal advice, but thankfully no threats of physical harm, the names of these giants of television have been removed by some spineless lawyers.)*

Five minutes of staring at these luminaries from the world of stage and screen, was more than enough to demolish any self-confidence amassed during a four night run in Richmond.

'You can go in now,' said Cheryl, the delightfully efficient secretary, in-between taking phone calls and messages.

Rex knocked timidly on the door of the office. There was no turning back.

'Come in.'

Taking a very deep breath, trying to slow down a racing heart, Rex turned the door handle, gulped, and entered as requested. Behind a big wooden desk, sat in an oversized chair was the big cheese, le grand fromage, the one and only star maker himself - Crispin Hansen.

'Come in here, dear boy. Pull up a chair.'

Rex did just that. He refused the generous offer of a cigar but opted instead for a healthier cup of tea. Cheryl was duly instructed to hold all calls when she returned with the tea and a plate of biscuits.

So it began…

'Rex, I saw your performance in Richmond last week, someone tipped me off about you. I was impressed. I think you might have something.'

'Thank you, sir.'

This was going well.

'What are your ambitions, Rex?'

Now there **is** a question. Do you go for the obvious answer: *"International fame, global domination and TWO Oscars, one for best actor and one for best dressed actor,"* thus proving you have the hunger to think big???

Alternatively do you go for the truth, which is that you really love acting and merely want to prove to yourself that you can do it.

The truth is always the best option...

'I love being an actor, sir. I like playing different characters, the escapism, working with other creative people. It's all I want to do.'

Simple. Refreshing. Innocent.

'I like you, Rex,' said Crispin, in response. 'I was watching you at the merchandise stand after the play last week. You were chatting away to the crowd, no airs, no graces, and they loved you for it. That's the secret you see, the public love someone down-to-earth they can relate to. Not only that, the British people always love an underdog; they love to see triumph over adversity. The Americans love a star, someone bigger than life itself. It's a different mindset altogether.'

This was all going far better than expected. So good, that Rex leaned forward and grabbed a digestive. He fancied a bit of a dunking session.

'What have you got coming up at the moment?' asked Crispin as Rex took a bite of his biscuit.

'Erm…Gordon Campbell has given me the lead role in his next play, so I start rehearsing that in November and, er…maybe a bit of panto in Wimbledon at Christmas. That's all really.'

Crispin laughed.

'Gordon, Gordon, Gordon,' he chuckled, looking at the ceiling and pushing himself back into his executive chair.

'I know Gordon. He's a bit of a luvvie, but I think you can do better than that.'

Crispin paused, rubbed his chin in deep thought as he rested an elbow on his gigantic and somewhat impressive chair.

'Rex, have you heard of Thomas Mueller?'

'No, sir.'

'Do you play football?'

'Of course, sir.'

'Well look, indulge me in this analogy if you will.'

Rex surveyed the plate of biscuits in front of him…*'Ooh, ginger nuts!...indulge away.'*

'You see, Gordon is your Sunday morning kick-about kind of chap. An orange at half-time, a few drinks with the boys down the Dog & Duck after the game, then back home for a full roast dinner. Good fun. Comfortable. Nothing wrong with that at all.'

Rex nodded in complete agreement. Sounds perfect!

Crispin continued…

'On the other hand, Thomas Mueller is more your Cup Final kind of guy. He'll have you up at 6am, raw eggs for breakfast and then he'll drag you out on a five mile run. All of this before you even get on the pitch. You'll train hard all week, working, working, working to get it right for the big match. Then, come Saturday afternoon at three o'clock, you kick-off at Wembley Stadium in front of a throbbing mass of people. You're playing the game of your life, knocking the ball all over the park with pinpoint precision. The crowd go wild as you dribble past four other players and chip the keeper from 30-yards, scoring a classic winner in the dying minutes of a two-one thriller. The fans chant your name as the ref blows the final whistle, and your team-mates carry you back to the dressing room on their shoulders. When you get there, the manager comes in, pats you on the back, and gives you a big, fat cash bonus. That manager is Thomas Mueller…do you see what I'm saying, Rex?'

Rex was already there, being carried around the stadium, waving his number three shirt above his head as the fans chanted over and over again: *"Roman, Roman, Roman"*.

'Rex…Rex?'

'Sorry, sir. I was thinking about what you said. Er...I don't like eggs, can I have some cereal for breakfast instead?'

'What I'm saying Rex, is that Thomas is in a totally different league to Gordon. Do you want to play in the Cup Final, or do you prefer a Sunday morning kick-about with your mates?'

Rex paused, trying to think of a suitable answer.

'Can I have a kick-about with some mates in the Cup Final, sir?'

Crispin roared with laughter.

'You see Rex, that's what I like about you. Most people would have chosen one or the other, a clean-cut decision. You, my young friend, still want to play with your mates but at the highest level. It's a fudge of them both. Good answer.'

Rex hadn't thought of it like that. He just wanted to have fun with friends, be it in a game of football or acting on a stage.

'Rex, have you got a passport?'

'Yes, sir.'

'Good, go home, get it, and come back here for five o'clock. I'm going to make some phone calls. I think we can really do something with you.'

Rex put his empty cup back on the desk and left the office. This had been quite some interview. Cup of tea, five biscuits, handsome agent with a large chair - what more could any aspiring actor want? Now all Rex had to do was go home and collect his passport.

'OH NO, the passport!!!...'

Chapter 25 – The Passport

Tuesday 3rd August 1976

'How did it go, honey?' asked an excited Lucy, bounding up to meet Rex as he came in through the front door.

Rex didn't look quite as happy as she had hoped, so she assumed the interview hadn't gone too well.

'Aah sweetheart, it'll be all right. You'll find another agent who will see your potential, the same as I do.'

'I have to go back at five o'clock with my passport,' said Rex, his face drained of colour. 'He's going to help me.'

'Honey, that is brilliant! See, I believe in you, and now some big-time agent does, too. All that worrying was for nothing. You can do this.'

Earlier that morning, Lucy had rung her boss at the bank and explained she wasn't going into work today. Rex had a big interview, so she wanted to be with him before and after, to lend her support. By a remarkable coincidence her boss was also her Dad, Peter, who also supported Rex, so it didn't cause a problem.

Rex ate some baked beans *with* toast for lunch, had a cup of tea and watched a bit of telly with Stanley. Before long, it was time for the return journey to see Crispin Hansen…

* * *

As Rex sat in the reception of CH Entertainments, admiring the famous faces hanging on the wall, he noticed a photo of *Rod Hull & Emu* next to one of *'Parky'*. Crispin dealt with both ends of the entertainment spectrum. There was hope!

'Come in,' boomed a well-spoken voice.

Rex entered Crispin's office and sat down.

'Everything all right? You look a bit peaky,' said Crispin, noticing that Rex was not quite as keen on the biscuits as he had been earlier.

'I'm fine, sir,' replied Rex.

'Good. Well, I've been busy on your behalf since you left. I've spoken to Thomas Mueller, and he has agreed to take you through some intensive training. We want to assess your abilities and your aptitude for acting. Thomas runs a theatre school, you see. I trust him totally. I've known him for years. It's a tough business Rex, but if he says you're good enough to be in it, then I will do everything I can for you.'

Rex was sort of listening, but he was much more distracted than he had been earlier that day. He had heard *"Thomas... acting...theatre"*, and they were probably the key words anyway.

'So, did you bring your passport?'

Rex did have the passport, but this was no official at a ferry terminal with his hand out. This was a proper agent who had the keys to open all the correct doors. Rex took the passport out of his back pocket, placed it on the desk and slid it slowly towards Crispin. He was about to be exposed, so he sat and awaited his fate, shuffling uneasily in his chair, with a face that looked like he was sucking a lemon.

'Oh, I see,' said Crispin, reading the identity details inside. 'So, Rex Roman is your stage name…brilliant…this other one is bloody awful!'

Rex laughed and spat out the lemon.

'Look, Rex. I'll let you in on my own secret. **My name is not** really Crispin.'

'Crikey! That's an unexpected revelation. Maybe he's a woman?'

'No, my real name is Christopher Hansen. Do you know what? No one remembers a Christopher. Sure there's that Christopher Wren fellow who built St. Paul's, but who else? It's even worse to be called Chris. So, I decided to change my name to Crispin Hansen years ago, before I really started in this business. People will always remember a Crispin. It's all in the name, Rex.

Rex was enlightened. *'Crispin, you wily old dog you.'*

'People will remember Rex Roman. I couldn't have thought of a better name myself. It doesn't matter what they say about you Rex, as long as they spell your name correctly. I can tell you have sat down and really thought about this for hours, days, possibly weeks…well done, I'm impressed.'

'Thank you, sir,' replied Rex, grateful for the approval.

'BUT, there is one big difference between you and I.'

That was fairly obvious. Crispin had an office in the centre of London, a secretary, a large chair, famous clients' faces on his walls, wealth, power, influence and he was well-respected within the acting business.

'My passport is in the name of Crispin Hansen. All traces of Christopher have been erased. Would you like me to arrange that for you?'

'How do you do that, sir?'

'Look, I've got a lawyer chap I use for all my legal stuff, Ben. He will deal with all of this for you. Within a couple of weeks or so, you'll get a new passport. The new one will be in the sole name of Rex Roman. You will never have to worry again. It'll be our little secret.'

'As easy as that?'

'It's as simple as that, my boy. You'll have to sign a few papers and pose for a laughably bad photo, but I'll get Cheryl to call you when you need to come in to sort that lot out. It will all be done just in time I expect.'

'Just in time for what, sir?' Rex was paying full attention now.

'You're going to Germany. You're going to study acting in Hamburg with Thomas Mueller for two months. Did I not mention that bit?'

'Not exactly.'

'Don't worry, my boy. Thomas speaks perfect English. I only send the best young actors over to see him, away from the harsh glare of London's critics. It's my investment in your potential. He'll take good care of you, I promise. This whole experience will completely change the way you think about acting.'

Rex couldn't believe this. In only a few hours he had secured the services of a new agent, a new passport and now had an opportunity to study at a theatre school. Why do key moments keep arriving in 3s?

* * *

This time when Rex returned home, it was as though a totally different person had walked through the front door. Overjoyed with excitement, he sat Lucy down on the sofa and told her the whole story.

He skilfully missed out the whole passport identity scenario, knowing that his secret was concealed forever. Finally, legally and forever more, he would be Rex Roman.

Rex declared it was time to open the Battenberg cake, which had been safely stored for 'special occasions'. This one easily qualified, and a celebration was in order. It was time to woof down some of the good stuff.

'I'll make a cup of tea, honey,' said Lucy, 'it'll help to wash down the cake.'

Once Rex had cut the marzipan-based treat into several large slices, he sat on the sofa trying to digest his luck...and his cake. When Lucy returned, she handed Rex a cup of tea. The look in her eyes said everything. She was so proud of her man.

At that point, Rex realised that Lucy was the one that had made all of this happen. Her love and her belief had convinced him to attend the interview with Crispin. Her love and support had made him work harder for his dream. Lucy empowered Rex, and he knew that he was a very lucky man to have such a wonderful woman in his life.

From that day forward, if ever Lucy said: 'Shall I make a cup of tea?'

Rex would reply: 'Will there be any love in it?'

He would always smile as she said: 'Of course, honey.'

A drink with love is not something you can ever hope to buy. It can only ever be made by someone who loves you. When you are handed the cup, look in the eyes of that special person and you will understand. Once you see the look, you can taste the love, and then no other drink is ever going to be anywhere near as good.

Chapter 26 – Time To Get Serious

Sep - Oct 1976

Hamburg is a fantastic German city, set on the water in the North of the country. 'Bomber' Harris and Grandad Bill did give it a bit of a battering during the War, but the industrious German people have rebuilt it in a glorious fashion.

Rex thought the flight from London to Hamburg was especially memorable. The joy of checking in at Heathrow airport, as *Mr Rex Roman,* for his first-ever flight, was a landmark moment. The *free* bag of in-flight nibbles was also fairly significant.

Thomas went to collect Rex from the airport. The German mentor was instantly spotted due to his clever use of a piece of cardboard and a marker pen, which had been combined to spell - ROMAN. Leaving the airport, Rex burst into fits of laughter when the car park cashier kindly wished him a *"gute fahrt"*. Thomas explained that this meant *"good trip"* and was not at all wind related. Displaying his maturity, Rex still chuckled for most of the ride into the city.

Thomas was not a tall man, about 5-foot, 5-inches, but what he lacked in height he gained in stature. Rex felt that he was in the presence of a master. Thomas had intense brown eyes and a pair of round, John Lennon style glasses. Curiously, he also had a triangular tuft of hair under his bottom-lip. Rex wondered if it was real or not, and only a tug test would tell.

After settling into his very basic but clean room, close to the school, Rex had an *"altitude sickness"* recovery snooze for about an hour. When he woke up, it was time for dinner.

In the university area of Hamburg, there is a really popular restaurant called Abaton. It was here that Thomas and Rex had their first meal together. *(The restaurant is still there now. If you go, then try the chicken with cashew nuts, vegetables and rice. It's delicious.)* Over dinner, Rex and Thomas began to discuss what lay ahead…

'So what makes you think you can be an actor, Mr Roman?' asked Thomas, staring intensely, waiting for a good answer.

'My girlfriend, Crispin Hansen and my heart, sir.'

Thomas stroked his mini-beard and nodded his head in approval. 'Good! Love, a well-connected mentor and plenty of self-belief. Three magical ingredients.'

Rex made an impressive start. Over the next ninety minutes as the conversation flowed, he learnt more about the art of the mind than he had in a year of tuition with Gordon.

Close to the Abaton restaurant is a cinema. In 1976, this cinema was actually a theatre school. A highly respected house of learning, owned and directed by one - Herr. T. Mueller.

The following day at 8am sharp, Rex was outside the school as instructed. When Thomas arrived with some breakfast, it signalled the start of a period of intensive training. Inside, the pair began some private one-to-one tuition.

'Now, Mr Roman, I want to do some role-play. I will create a character and give you a situation. You will act it out believing you **are** that character. You understand, yes?'

'Yes, sir.'

This was it. This was the first class with the master…

'Imagine you are a chicken, not any old chicken but the finest rooster in the yard. You are confident. You crow like a cock, and you own that yard. Come on, Rex. Be that chicken!'

Rex was expecting something slightly more conventional, but Thomas was the boss. What the master said: the student did, so Rex started to strut. A minute of strutting around the stage ensued, accompanied by Thomas shouting...

'Give me more chicken! I'm not feeling it. This is a duck, not a rooster I am seeing. Be that chicken, Rex. Be that chicken!!!'

Three additional minutes of guidance transformed Rex, from a chicken too scared to cross the road, into a confident King Rooster rollerskating down the German autobahn.

'Bravo!' shouted Thomas. 'I thought you were going to lay an egg. That was hilarious.'

Rex actually thought it was a bit embarrassing, but he was there to learn so he didn't question it.

Once he'd wiped the tears from his eyes, the master spoke…

'That of course was not about acting. That was about control. For the next eight weeks, I control you. What I say, you do. I wanted to see if you would do this. To be a true actor you must know no shame. You are shameless!'

A light went on inside Rex's mind that morning. He was never going to pursue a career as a professional chicken, but with this man's help, he might just get a professional career.

Back in London, Lucy was lonely without her mate. Bradley missed his best friend, Kate felt teary and even Roy said the house wasn't the same without young Rex popping over. These were the days before the internet made communication easier, email didn't even exist, and telephone calls back home were infrequent due to huge costs.

Two months later, Rex returned to England to be greeted at Heathrow by Lucy and Bradley. Lucy cried when she saw Rex and spent the entire journey home smothering him with kisses and cuddles. Bradley just smiled an enormous grin, flashing those immaculate gnashers of his.

Back in the comfortable surroundings of chez Roman, Stanley pecked his bell like a budgie possessed at the sight of Daddy. When the family settled down to watch some television after dinner, Stanley took his position on Daddy's right shoulder, Lucy snuggled up to Rex's left.

Rex had gone to Germany knowing only three German phrases:

1. 'Ja' ***(Yes)***
2. 'Nein' ***(No)***

and the inexplicable:

3. 'Ich habe eine kartoffel' ***(I have a potato)***

Only two of them proved useful.

Rex came home with a few more phrases under his belt, but this was secondary to what he had learned about himself and his art. Lights were on, fires were burning and Rex was raring to go.

Rex had the stuff alright. Now he just needed a break…

Chapter 27 – Networking

November 1976

Fresh back from Germany, Rex had to set about the serious task of finding some decent acting roles. His current schedule included three weeks of panto at Christmas and the lead role in Gordon Campbell's next comedy production, The Ghost & Mr Chicken. Gorden had rewritten the original script, from the classic 1966 film, to stage yet another unique production. Rex wasn't really sure if he was The Ghost or Mr Chicken, but he was versatile.

Thomas had sent glowing reports back to London, and Crispin knew for sure that Rex was totally serious, totally dedicated and had a good head on his shoulders. He was well-balanced, and the perfect material to be moulded into a fine actor; he just needed some paid work.

Crispin decided that his new client should be tutored in the art of networking. At the office of CH Entertainments, he tried to explain the inner workings of the business...

'Rex, this business is partly about what you know, but more importantly, it's about **who** you know. Luckily, you know me.'

'Yes, sir.'

'So let me explain a few things about how this business works.'

'Okay, sir.'

Rex was all ears…

'Firstly, if people don't know who you are, they won't listen to you. So, you have to get yourself attached to something that attracts their attention. No one is going to be brave enough to invest millions of pounds into a film, TV series or stage production using some actor they've never even heard of, no matter how talented the actor may be. Industry big-wigs all want to keep their jobs and more importantly…their money.'

Rex nodded, got it so far.

'So what you do is star in something that's a runaway success, then everyone wants a piece of you. They're lining up around the block to make you offers, and your agent, ME, exists to filter those offers on your behalf...for a very modest 15% fee. Today's: *"Please don't call me again!"* rejection, is tomorrow's: *"I always knew you were talented! I've always believed in you!! Let's do lunch!!!".'*

'Great, I understand. So how do I get the role in the first place?' asked Rex, fully grasping the concept.

'You can't! No one will take your phone call as they've never heard of you.'

The wheels were spinning in Rex's head, but sadly, the hamster had died of exhaustion trying to keep up with the confusing world of showbiz.

'It's all one big *chicken and the egg* scenario, Rex.'

Rex was beginning to wonder if the entire acting industry was obsessed with poultry.

Crispin continued...

'However, I do have a plan to get you laying a few eggs. I am going to teach you about the dark arts of *The Schmooze* and *The Embellishment.*'

Examples of:

The Schmooze
You need to know where fellow actors, celebrities and people of power hang out. Find out where they're either performing, networking or simply relaxing. They too, need the oxygen of publicity to maintain their own profiles. Find out where they eat, drink or generally socialise. Get your best clothes on, appropriate to the occasion, and get out there and make an impression. It's about how you carry yourself. Let them know who you are. If you don't believe in your talent, then no one else is going to. Why should they?

The Embellishment
There are two answers to the common question:

"What have you been working on lately?"

Answer 1: The Truth
I have been studying at a theatre school over in Germany, dancing around like a chicken, desperately trying to improve my knowledge so that someone will hire me for a job. Please hire me, please!!!

Answer 2: The Embellishment
'I have been starring in a major theatrical production in Germany. I had a demanding role, which was a huge success, and my agent is currently in negotiations with a top director for future contracts.'

The Embellishment is based on the truth, like those books and films that are *based on a true story.* There's always some truth in there somewhere, but it's all about creative licence. It's all fantasy. Acting is pretending, and the whole business is built on pretending. It's otherwise known as **'Entertainment'.**

* * *

That evening, Rex and Crispin went out to *Schmooze* around London. If influential people saw Rex with Crispin, it meant that they would notice this new face around town. Crispin was a serious player in the business, and serious players seem to attract attention wherever they go.

Crispin paid well over the odds for drinks in all manner of places, but this was all part of the *"egg laying"* as he called it.

There are a number of watering holes in London where many from the luvvie community habitually go for a post-play tipple. That night, most of these pubs and clubs were home to some lavishly tall stories. Rex felt like a young apprentice engaged in serious training with Yoda, and he was feeling the Force. *(We know that Star Wars didn't come out until December '77 in the UK, but this is all part of The Embellishment of the story... see, it's that easy to do!)*

'What now?' asked Rex as the evening came to its natural conclusion.

'We go out again another night, then again and again. It's a war of attrition, Rex. You may lose a few battles but if you just keep fighting, eventually, someone will surrender.'

'Then what?'

'Well, my boy. Then you get your chance. I will have done my part, and the rest is up to you. I can only create the opportunity. You are the one that must seize the day.'

Rex and Crispin went out many times over the following month. Rex didn't really feel that comfortable with the whole pretending *Embellishment* thing, he was far too honest for such truth bending. He was also shy with strangers and would much rather have been relaxing at home with his family: Lucy and Stanley.

As a professional agent, Crispin was an expert in the art of smoke and mirrors, so Rex let him do all the talking. They both heard loads of wild gossip, true or false, Rex didn't care, until he heard one piece of hearsay that he couldn't ignore.

Once Rex told Bradley the breaking news, it was clear that they had another adventure on their hands…

Chapter 28 – A Bloke Called Terry

December 1976

Rex Roman has two secret shames. The **first** is his fascination with the decorative, artistic layout of the fish counter at his local supermarket. The **second** is the day he nearly caused a catastrophe over London.

Following up a rumour overheard on a *Schmooze* with Crispin, Rex knew that Pink Floyd were going to hold a photoshoot for their forthcoming album *Animals.* The location for this event was to be Battersea Power Station.

Apparently, the band planned to have a 30-foot inflatable pig flown above the station, once it had been safely attached to the ground by a wire. Floating in the air, this giant pork kite would make a fabulous iconic image that could hopefully be immortalised on the album cover, for promotional purposes.

Bradley had confirmed this rumour as 100% accurate as he had spoken to Roy about it. Roy had confirmed the rumour because he personally knew the trained marksman that was going to be on-site, in case of any mishaps.

Naturally!

Battersea Power Station is not actively used anymore. It is not one but two separate power stations (A & B) that are linked together. Station A was decommissioned from service in 1975, after 42 years supplying electricity to the capital. Not a lot of people know that unless they have actually been there, seen it with their own eyes or spoken to a bloke called Terry.

If you ever happen to be travelling on the train into Waterloo, *(perhaps to start that romantic tour? - see page 113)* you will easily spot its four majestic chimneys that dominate the skyline just before Vauxhall station. It's not until you get up close, that you can truly appreciate the enormous size of this classic London landmark and its towering chimneys.

'Boy, am I looking forward to this,' said Bradley, parking his Mini in the vicinity of the power station, ready for the day's ambitious photoshoot.

'Me too,' replied Rex. 'So, where shall we go?'

'Roy said if we go and see Terry, then he'll tell us where to stand for the best view.'

'Who's Terry?' asked Rex, wondering how Bradley had such great inside information.

'Terry is the marksman. Roy reckons he's an expert shot.'

After stumbling around the perimeter fence for a while, Rex and Bradley saw a man wearing blue overalls who seemed to fit the profile of a trained marksman.

'Are you Terry?' asked Bradley.

'Who wants to know?' was the terse reply.

'My Dad says: **"If it moves, shoot it!"**.'

'Well why didn't you say that in the first place?' replied Terry, immediately becoming more animated and less threatening. 'You must be Bradley and Rex. I've been expecting you two.'

'That was easy,' thought Rex.*'One password and we both have immediate acceptance into the murky world of contract killers.'*

Rex was mystified; something funny was going on here. Roy's trademark was written all over this set-up, but surely his best friend wasn't colluding in an evil plot to finish him off? How did Terry know Rex's name? Why was he expecting them both? Looking for clues, Rex realised there must be some secret message written into Bradley's 'I'm With Stoopid' T-shirt.

'Right, you stick with me, lads. I'll get you the best view in the house. If anything goes wrong, I have to take the pig out with this,' said Terry, tapping the barrel of the long rifle that was slung over his right-shoulder.

The pair followed Terry into position and waited, and waited, and............................ waited...

* * *

'Not quite as exciting as we thought,' said Bradley. 'What's the hold-up?'

'Well, it's all the preparations,' responded Terry, 'this ain't your regular porker, this is a whopper. We're talking about thirty foot of inflatable air hazard. That pig could take down a plane if it flew into an engine.'

'Oh, that makes sense,' agreed Rex, 'best be safe then.'

'Exactly!' replied Terry, tapping his rifle for reassurance.

The thing about hanging around for hours and hours is that you soon get bored. Eventually the pig did go up, and it was quite a spectacle... for a couple of minutes, but once you've seen one giant inflatable pig hanging over an iconic piece of London real estate, you've seen them all.

'Is that it then?' said Rex, having spent a full two minutes staring at the spectacle.

'That's it,' replied Terry.

'Oh.'

'What did you expect?'

'I don't know really. I thought I might see one of the band or something,' said Rex, underwhelmed by the pig.

'No, no they're far too important to be hanging around out here with the likes of us,' stated Terry. 'They'll be somewhere warm and comfortable I expect. All those musicians and actors have such great lives.'

'I'm an actor!' gushed Rex, finding something of interest for his new gangland brother.

'REALLY?' Terry suddenly became very excited. 'What have you been working on lately?'

The perfect time for an *Embellishment…*

'I have been starring in a major theatrical production in Germany. I had a demanding role, which was a huge success, and my agent is currently in negotiations with a top director for future contracts.'

Delivered like a pro. Crispin would have been so proud.

'Aah, I've always wanted to be an actor myself,' revealed Terry, gazing at the greyish sky momentarily, before continuing his one-way conversation. 'I've had talks with some top people in the business you know. They've given me some advice on how to *stalk people* and how to *tell huge lies*, all the crafty little tricks. This is just a day-gig until I get my big break.'

Feeling passionate about his own thespian ambitions, Terry then began to assault Rex and Bradley with a never-ending monologue about his history in acting, his career to-date and where he was going to be in five years.

Once the heavy artillery of hype had stopped, Terry caught his breath, before launching into the Top Ten reasons why he should be starring in *The Sweeney*. It was during this rant that Rex became a trifle concerned…

'5. I'm an expert shot, and I look convincing with a gun…'

'Er…Terry,' said Rex, anxiously.

'6. I can roll over a car bonnet and drive through cardboard boxes with the best of them…'

'Terry, I think we've got a problem.'

'7. That Carter is an absolute…'

'TERRY! The pig has escaped!!!'

Rex and Bradley pointed to the sky, where the large pig had broken free from its 'unbreakable' anchor and was heading off for a sightseeing trip over Central London. Terry had been so busy talking, he'd completely failed to spot the giant pink sow doing a runner.

'Christ, it's out of range!' shouted Terry, aiming his rifle with the steely eye of a trained killer as he targeted the runaway. When he lowered his rifle without discharging a single bullet, Terry uttered a menacing line…

'Heads are gonna roll for this one.'

When a slightly unhinged man, armed with a gun, stands next to you and declares: *"Heads are gonna roll…"* it's probably a good time to leave.

These 'Chain' inducing words ensured Rex's departure and he sped off like a rocket, dragging a bewildered Bradley behind him. Rex insisted they drive back home as quickly as the Mini could take them while watching for any flying bacon overhead. He spent the afternoon at chez Milwee, worrying, unable to focus properly on a game of *Speed Monopoly*. Bradley on the other hand, thought the whole scenario was outrageously funny, and he was keen to tell Roy all about it.

The *tail* of the flying pig made it onto the local London news, the national news and into the papers the next day. Luckily no planes did fly into the pork related air hazard, although one pilot reported a sighting, only to be later questioned about his drinking habits. The escaped pig eventually came down harmlessly in Kent, after several hours of aimless floating.

Well, when we say harmlessly, it did actually crash into a barn, causing a not inconsiderable amount of damage, but at least no one was injured. Terry's gross incompetence and his true identity were both covered up by a few silky-smooth public relations people, with some of them laughably suggesting that he wasn't even present when the pig broke free. Only a handful of people in the world know what really happened that day...until now.

This is the shocking truth, allegedly, about the flying pig that escaped over London in December 1976.

The best-kept secret in rock history has finally been exposed and made public knowledge - at last! Rex has always felt bad about his part in the saga, and that is why the event has been added to his 'secret shame list'.

Rex spent days afterwards, waiting for a knock at his front door from an angry Terry. He had cleverly deduced that Terry must be one of Roy's brutal henchmen, and as Bradley had so gleefully told Roy the whole story, then Rex's days were surely numbered. When there was a loud knock at the front door the following week, it was only Bradley. Rex was relieved to see his best friend, until he heard him speak...

'Dude, I'm leaving England. Roy is taking us all back to the States... FOREVER!'

* * *

Chapter 29 – The American Dream

Monday 24th January 1977

When someone you love dies, the pain of that loss is truly excruciating. When people you love tell you they are moving 1000s of miles away, the pain is still there, but it's different. Despite this pain, you still have the comfort of knowing that no matter how far the distance, efforts can be made to keep in touch. All is not lost. There is hope.

On a bitterly cold January day in 1977, Rex found himself at Heathrow airport with three people he really loved. They all had one-way tickets, and Rex didn't feel very hopeful about his future.

'I can't believe it, mate,' said Rex as he and Bradley sat in the departures terminal. 'I've been dreading this day, and now you're finally leaving.'

'I know, I know, I can't believe it either. We'll keep in touch though, we'll always be friends.'

Bradley and Rex had grown up together. They had learnt about life from one another and stood like brothers through thick and thin. They also both shared big dreams. In some ways Bradley was glad to be leaving London, so he too could follow his own dreams back home in America.

'At least I'll be able to get my music going again though, dude. When I'm a star you can come and live near me in the States, I'll buy you a house.'

This was a touching gesture. Sadly, the constantly bankrupt Bank of Bradley didn't look like it would be in a position to honour this gesture anytime soon.

After his Marquee gig disaster, and with the unstoppable rise in the popularity of punk rock, Bradley couldn't see any chance of getting a musical career in England. Bradley wanted to play rock music, and America was the home of rock. Bands like Aerosmith and Kiss were huge there, playing spectacular concerts, yet they were practically unheard of in Britain. This was what Bradley wanted, to be part of a spectacle.

Roy had been given a "new contract" in the States, and the whole family was heading back to Los Angeles. They had no plans to return to the UK. The thing about America is, that from England, it's a very long swim if you don't have the money to fly. Rex didn't have the money for luxury air travel. He did have a fetching pair of Speedos though, but they were best confined to the swimming pools of North London.

As the final moment approached, it was time for goodbyes…

'This is it then,' sighed Rex, resigned to defeat.

'Yeah, man. I'm gonna miss you, Lucy and CH. If anyone can make you a star, CH can. Then you can buy **me** a house.'

Roy, Kate and Bradley were all standing with Rex, a short distance from the departures gate. Emotionally, all four of them huddled together in a loving embrace that signalled goodbye. It wasn't just Bradley that had grown up with Rex. For Kate and Roy this was a sad farewell, too. They had seen both Rex and Bradley grow from boys into men and had pride in what they had become. This was the break-up of a tightknit unit; every member was choked and fighting back the tears.

'Take this,' said Roy, handing over a brown envelope.

'What is it, sir?' asked Rex, not knowing whether it was polite to look inside.

'Open it and you'll see.'

Inside the envelope was more money than Rex had seen for a long time. He was astonished by the generosity.

'There's a thousand pounds there, young man. That's enough for you and Lucy to come to the States and see us sometime. It doesn't matter when; you'll always be welcome in our family. You **are** family to us.'

This was the most touching thing that Rex had ever heard the big man say. He hugged him tightly, having abandoned the more formal handshake, such was the emotion.

'And stop calling me "sir" and get with the Roy thing. It's been ten years now for heaven's sake!'

The tension broke, and everyone laughed.

Thanks to Roy's generosity, Rex had some money to save for a rainy day. He intended to put it in a jam jar in his kitchen cupboard, just as Nan had. If he hadn't been taking his black belt examination in Kung Fu, only six weeks later, Rex might have immediately rushed home, grabbed Lucy and bought two tickets for the next available flight. As it was, his date with the LA sunshine would have to wait...........just a little while longer.

'By the way,' said Roy as he revealed one final surprise. 'There's two tickets in there, front row, to see Pink Floyd at Wembley in March.'

Rex was stunned.

'How did you...?'

'Don't ask, Rex. I'll tell you what though, the next time I see you, I'll tell you exactly how I got those tickets. I know you'll remember to ask me.'

With one final kiss for Kate, then another group hug, the Milwee family were gone.

* * *

Rex cried a few tears on the way back to the bus, he couldn't help it. He got back home and cried a few more until Stanley cheered him up by coming out to play. Lucy came home early from work, made Rex some dinner and fussed over him all evening. She even had a go at *Speed Monopoly,* but her limited skills offered little resistance to the corporate might of the Roman empire. Lucy felt sad that night as she too had grown fond of Bradley. The three of them were a gang. They were friends with a special bond, and they'd all be together again one day...they just hadn't set the date yet.

Chapter 30 – The First Fight

Saturday 19th March 1977

If there are any true Pink Floyd fans out there who say they have ***never*** played air guitar, to at least one of David Gilmour's legendary guitar solos, they are either:

a: Lying through their teeth.
b: NOT really a fan.

Come on loosen up a bit, admit it.

The more dedicated amongst you will almost certainly have utilised at least one of, if not all, the following implements to assist the dream:

a: Tennis Racquet.
b: Broom or Hoover Handle.
c: Guitar, be it inflatable or air.
d: Ruler – any size acceptable.
e: All of the above *(Well done).*

If by chance, you have fallen into the *NOT really a fan* category and you are desperate to raise your kudos, then it is strongly suggested that you grab any implement from the handy list above and get cracking.

Go on, try it. It's extremely good fun.

Rex Roman is a master with every implement on the list. Although it was after one particular practice session in 1977, that a tragedy forced the master's early retirement and nearly ended his glittering air guitar career.

* * *

It was nearly 11am on Saturday the 19th of March, 1977.

That same evening Rex and Lucy had two tickets, courtesy of Roy, to go and see Pink Floyd once again at Wembley Empire Pool.

Rex had spent the morning planning the concert agenda. He allowed sufficient time for hot dogs, T-shirt mulling and general merchandise selection. He even added an hour for the 'atmosphere before the show' enjoyment factor. This is defined as 'ambience soaking' in The Rexasaurus.
(The Rexasaurus is located in the front of this book. See notes page ix.)

Lucy had gone into Central London with Maureen to do some shoe shopping. She had promised Rex that she'd be back home by 3pm to allow enough time for their busy concert schedule.

As Rex had the house to himself with nothing meaningful to do, he'd decided that he should work on his art, like a master craftsman does. The inspirational literary works of many a fine writer and scholar were begging to be picked up from the bookcase. Unsurprisingly, these were completely ignored as Rex surveyed the extensive record collection with a mischievous glint in his eye. The term record collection does not adequately describe the tempting sonic flavours on offer; these albums were more like a smörgåsbord of opportunity for the serious air guitar enthusiast.

If you are partial to a bit of air tomfoolery, then Jimi Hendrix will serve you well. For Rex Roman, there is only one possible choice when selecting his favourite album of all time:

The Dark Side of the Moon

One track in particular on this album, **Time,** is the ultimate play-along for every true Pink Floyd fan. Let's examine the reasons why…

First, you get to play the drums at the start. This unique Roto-tom sound is a Nick Mason classic and a must-hear experience. The drumming is so rhythmically random that you will surely miss at least one of the notes in your solo, and you can always blame the ticking clocks for putting you off.

Once you have completed your drumming, you can then have a little sing-song with some truly inspired lyrics. Be prepared though, because you only have 59 seconds before your amazing one-and-a-half minute guitar solo. Have a couple of attempts at that little lot before you leave for work, and the crazy buzz will set you up for the day. **But,** if you really want to get serious about this, then like any craftsman, you will need the correct tools for the job.

Next to the front door at chez Roman, is an outside cupboard where all of the utility meters are housed. This is also the place where Rex keeps his broom collection, the tools of his air guitar trade.

Feeling overly confident, Rex had assembled some pots and pans in a tight semi-circle on the lounge carpet. He was about to fritter away the hours in his dull day for sure and hammer those suckers in true caveman style. Some wooden spoons were primed in the back pocket of his jeans, ready to assist the slaughter.

The clocks had begun ticking away at the start of the song, and with his meticulous assembly of the pots and pans, Rex had completely forgotten his guitar. He rushed outside, grabbed a broom, made a desperate dash back to his modified drum kit and whipped two spoons out of his back pocket. He only just made it in on time with Nick, phew, and proceeded to make loud banging noises, pulling funny faces from the sheer strain of his throbbing power. Tossing the spoons away after a furious 90 second solo, Rex switched to the broom, plugged it into his air Marshall amp, and the band played on. What a professional!

It was a virtuoso performance as Rex was so excited about the forthcoming concert that night. He hadn't seen Pink Floyd since the 16th of November 1974, over two years prior, and had missed the band's only 1975 show in the UK, due to his French holiday adventures with Lucy.

Stanley had a ringside seat in the stadium of dreams. He watched from the perch in his cage, nodding along as Daddy practised. The feathered fan had been in the house for nine months now; he'd seen it all before.

Now if you know anything about budgies, then you would know that these pets need their cages cleaned regularly - trill must be very high in fibre.

When Stanley first arrived, Lucy had made a pact that Rex never had to do any Stanley related chores, but now, nine months on, Rex felt that he was missing out on part of the family fun. He'd watched Lucy clean the budgie cage many times before and started thinking…

'Okay at the bottom of the cage is a tray which slides out…easy! Change the sandpaper in the tray, change his water and give him some fresh trill. How hard can it be?'

It is not entirely necessary to let a budgie out when you clean its cage, but Rex couldn't resist his green feathered friend. On a post-gig high, Rex decided him and Stanley should have some quality alone-time, by watching a spot of TV together. On her return, Lucy would see that the cage had been cleaned, Stanley had been fed and watered, and she'd be impressed that Rex had done it all by himself.

As the cage door was being opened, Stanley prepared to do his usual mad dash around the room before settling down to his viewing position on the sofa. Stupidly, Rex had forgotten to shut the lounge door, in his blind panic to get back to play the drums *(saucepans)* on cue with Nick.

The lounge door at chez Roman leads through to a hall, which leads to the front door, which then leads to the outside world. Stanley utilised all the open spaces and within seconds flew straight out into the street, much to Rex's horror.

The next couple of hours were spent wandering around the neighbourhood, looking for the much-loved bird. Rex thought there was a sighting in a tree, but how do you coax a budgie down from a tree? Sadly, that was the last he ever saw of his household pet.

When Lucy returned at 3pm and saw the cage, less one tenant, she was frantic. Rex couldn't explain that it was all his fault because he had been practising his guitar *(which was actually a broom)*. He'd only just had enough time to plug the guitar into his air Marshall amp *(which was invisible)* before his solo on the drums *(which were saucepans on the floor)*. In the heat of the moment, he had forgotten to shut the front door and Stanley had escaped. Somehow it just didn't sound right; it was too ridiculous, even though it was the truth.

This tragic tale of Stanley's escape is the **third and final** item on the Rex Roman 'secret shame list'.

Lucy was in tears and beside herself with grief. As strange as it may sound to some people, Stanley was more than a budgie; he was an important part of the family.

At 4pm it was time to go to the concert, even though Lucy was still distraught at the loss of her little boy.

Rex was in a pickle. The budgie had gone, but the greatest band in the world was on stage that night, and Rex had two tickets to see them.

'What time do you want to leave for the concert?' asked Rex very, very tentatively.

'I AM NOT GOING TO A CONCERT!!!'

Lucy was furious. She grabbed her coat and stormed out of the house, announcing that she was going to stay with her mother for a while. She gave no indication of when she would return as the door slammed behind her.

Rex went to the concert all by himself. He didn't have a hot dog as he was too upset to eat, although he did buy an 'official' programme which he read during the time spent 'ambience soaking' before the show.

What should have been the premium night of the year had become a complete disaster. Rex couldn't even begin to enjoy the concert as he felt saddened by the day's events. There he was at a Pink Floyd show without Bradley or Lucy, and now he had a home without Stanley.

As much as Rex loved the band, he loved his girlfriend more, and after the first song, he left. He went to Maureen's to try and patch things up, but Lucy wouldn't come to the door. Maureen suggested that Rex should let the situation calm down for a few days, and everything would be all right in the end.

Rex followed the advice, went stir crazy for a couple of days, and then came up with a cunning plan. He went to the local pet shop and bought a striking yellow budgerigar, in an attempt to fill the empty void that Stanley had left. Well, the house was just never going to be the same without the pitter patter of tiny feet.

After four days full of shame and regret, Rex turned up at Maureen's with the new family addition. Luckily, Lucy was really pleased to see her fool of a boyfriend who then speedily announced his retirement from the world of air guitar. She was even more pleased to see the surprise feathered gift and totally agreed with the colour choice; Stanley was far too special to be replaced with a substitute lookalike.

'What shall we call him?' asked Lucy as she looked across to the coffee table, staring lovingly at the yellow bird happily tweeting away in its cage.

'It's not a him, it's a her. Let's call her Twinkle,' suggested Rex. 'She's a star, just like you.'

'What do you mean?'

'Well, I was in the garden last night looking at the stars, and it made me think of my favourite nursery rhyme. Then that made me think of you, so I changed the words to fit my mood. Listen…'

Lucy was hardly prepared for the next part of the evening. Rex grabbed her hand, got down on one knee and sang, yes sang, the especially adapted nursery rhyme...

Twinkle Twinkle Little Star
How I wonder where you are
Crazy diamond in my sky
Up above the world so high
Twinkle Twinkle Little Star
How I love you as you are

Sniff... beautiful.

Lucy wept and threw her arms around Rex while Maureen clapped. Even Peter stopped reading the share price index in the newspaper, nodding in acknowledgement towards the young crooner.

Rex's original suggestion of Twinkle was shortened to Twinky, because Lucy thought this was a far catchier name for her new baby.

That night, the family Roman were all back together under one roof. Lucy, Rex and now... Twinky.

Chapter 31 – The Wedding

Saturday 10th June 1978

Rex had a childhood friend, his name was Bradley.

Lucy had a childhood friend, her name was Helen.

Today, on the 10th of June 1978, Helen was getting married.

Rex had initially been reluctant to attend the wedding, his main excuse being that he barely knew any of the other guests. He also found it hard to believe that Helen had chosen to get married while the World Cup football tournament was being played in Argentina. How inconsiderate was that?

Having abandoned his futile protest, Rex played his part to keep Lucy happy and got dressed up in his best outfit. This day meant a lot to her, and Lucy meant a lot to him, so it was the least he could do.

Lucy was absolutely thrilled about the wedding day, particularly as Helen's baby was due in six months. As the chief bridesmaid, Lucy had a big part to play in the day's success. She took her role seriously, and everyone commented on how gorgeous she looked in her dress.

A traditional church service gave Rex the perfect opportunity to yawn frequently, mumble along with some hymns and generally pretend that he was interested. His main thought throughout the whole ceremony was whether it would all be finished in time for the France versus Hungary game, which was scheduled for a 5.45pm kick-off.

After the service, all of the guests moved to Hendon Social Club for the reception. This large venue proved a good choice, with a main bar for the club's regular drinkers and another large function room for those attending the wedding party. Around the main bar, a noisy crowd was watching football on the club's television set with France storming to a 3-1 victory. In the function room, Disco Kev was setting up his somewhat tatty looking P.A. speakers and record decks, ready to play the latest hits of the day.

Disco Kev was from Birmingham, and his thick Brummie accent was not naturally conducive to the giddy world of showbiz. It was extremely difficult to understand any word that Kev said. He would often start a monotone sentence, only to lose his chain of thought halfway through. Thankfully, his indistinguishable mumblings of *"yow'll loik this one..."* were limited during the evening. The songs just kept on coming, disco hit after disco hit. Well, it was 1978.

Luckily for Disco Kev, no one seemed to mind his inane babble as all of the wedding guests were up for a good time. Helen's new husband was a man mountain, called Martin O'Connor. He and most of the other attendees were of fine Irish descent, which meant they had livers twice as hardy as the average drinker. The male guests were fond of a good pint or six, and the women weren't shy of a tipple or two either. By 9pm, the party was boisterously in full swing.

Rex stuck with the soft drinks all night, on account of his tragic medical condition *"Floppy Limbosis"*. He got a bit of stick from Patrick O'Brien, who called him a big girl's blouse, but it was all light-hearted enough. Rex took no offence, stuck to his guns and to his orange juice. The main advantage of having less liquid in his stomach meant that Rex had more free space to cram in extra food, so he made full use of the vacancy and tucked into the generous spread on offer.

It was here in Hendon, North London, on a hot sweaty Saturday night in 1978, that Rex discovered the joy that is a 'vol-au-vent'. A remarkable puff pastry, with so many varieties of savoury fillings to choose from - this was some fancy living!

Rex often joked to Lucy that the only good reason for getting married was the three-tiered wedding cake. He had a sweet tooth for marzipan and as Tesco Supermarkets had started selling it in blocks, this kind of negated the whole argument for marriage. For some bizarre reason, Lucy didn't find that joke even remotely funny.

When Disco Kev played the Village People's classic tune, Macho Macho Man, Rex decided that this was his calling. Old snake hips went straight onto the dance floor to strut his funky stuff and redefine the boundaries of dance. The beat was pumping muddily through the speakers, yet Rex still set a trail-blazing pace with all of his best moves. He swung Granny O'Connor around as though she was a woman twenty years younger, and Aunt Mary nearly had a seizure laughing at such gymnastics. If Rex could burn off some extra calories, then he could justify one more slice of cake. Subsequently, the man was on fire.

Lucy loved it. Her guest was joining in the fun, and she even got to experience a few bouts of dance floor twirling at the hands of Fergal O'Connor. The low point of the evening was when Disco Kev played the Wurzels' hit, I've Got A Brand New Combine Harvester. This baffling song, with its catchy chorus, proved that alcohol really does impair judgment. The most memorable record that night was The Commodores sentimental smash, Three Times A Lady. Rex had the honour of dancing with Lucy, leading her round and round in a small circle, holding her tightly and treading on her toes from time to time.

By the end of the evening Rex was fluent in the traditional Irish anthem, Danny Boy. He was singing along and swaying away at a table in the main bar with the best of them, having clearly benefited from all of Crispin's good advice about networking and influencing people.

Such diplomatic skills did come in useful when Rex was a witness to some Helicopter Fighting. This alcohol induced martial art is practised the length and breadth of Britain most nights of the week, but more frequently on Friday and Saturday. It's the national sport of choice.

Helicopter Fighting involves two individuals squaring up to each other after both having consumed at least six pints of beer. The ritual usually begins with some finger pointing, a spot of light shouting closely followed by some sideways staggering, and then comes the good bit…

With mighty effort, the combatants start to swing their arms in a circular fashion. Heavy breathing and puffed up cheeks stir up the emotions as the arms begin to mimic the actions of a pair of blades, hence the appropriate name:

Helicopter Fighting

The source of discontent that began this evening's showdown between the whirling warriors was unknown. As is often the case with most practitioners of this ancient form of combat, they didn't need a good reason; they just needed a good drink.

As the rotors reached top speed and bags of pork scratchings fell from the wall behind the main bar, caught in the powerful draught from the flailing limbs, Rex soberly walked through the spinning air to try and intervene…

'Come on, lads. This is Helen and Martin's special day. Let's not spoil it.'

Common sense prevailed, and as the rotors wound back down to stationary, Rex was congratulated for his diplomacy. He was escorted to the bar by Uncle Brendan, who worryingly declared his love for Rex in slurred tones. As Rex sipped his orange juice, laughter filled the room again. A needless fight had been safely averted. Another bout of Danny Boy ensured the jovial atmosphere resumed as though nothing had ever happened.

Lucy and Helen were completely oblivious to the drama next door and were in the function room contemplating the day's events...

'Thank you so much, Lucy. You were brilliant. I've had such a fantastic day. I'm so happy I'm married,' enthused Helen. She and Lucy were sat around a table, while Disco Kev packed up his battered old equipment in the background.

'I am so happy for you,' gushed Lucy. 'I cried when you said "I do". It was wonderful.'

Having finished an out of tune We Are Sailing sing-a-long with Patrick O'Brien and the gang, Rex came over to the table.

'Hello ladies, it's been a great day hasn't it?' said Rex, still sober but exhausted. His tie was knotted around his forehead, giving him a mature almost statesman-like appearance. His shirt was half-open, and he was in buoyant mood.

Lucy looked at Rex, laughed and reeled him in by the tie to kiss him on the lips. The statesman grimaced at this public display of affection and made a hapless effort to escape the clinch, trying to maintain some manly dignity in front of the jeering Patrick O'Brien.

'I can't wait for you two to get married,' said Helen excitedly. 'How long has it been now?'

'Three years, six months and nine days,' replied Lucy as quick as a flash.

This struck Rex as a very detailed answer. Most men would have either rounded it up to *"nearly four years"* or rounded it down to *"just over three and a half years"*, but Lucy had counted the time exactly. It must have been all of that mathematical experience she'd gained from working in a bank.

'I believe in a long test drive,' chuckled Rex, thinking he was hilarious...as the tumbleweed rolled across the dance floor.

Helen raised an eyebrow and gave Lucy a knowing look. Lucy surveyed her boyfriend in all his disco glory, shook her head and smiled. Rex might be a plonker, but he was a loveable plonker, and Lucy knew he was prone to poor jokes. What was much more important for Lucy was that they were together. He would probably realise sooner or later why the coffee table at home was strewn with information about weddings and babies.

Rex never did seem to understand subtle hints.

* * *

Top Rex Tip 2: *When at a wedding/party or on holiday, it is worth remembering that thirty minutes of dancing buys the calorie tokens for one extra slice of cake. So get those fingers pointing, snake hips thrusting and get down to the crazy beat - unless it's the 'Okey Cokey'.*

All things in life 'Okey' are best avoided. 'Okey Cokey', 'Okey Dokey', and don't even attempt the Russian version, 'Okski Dokski'. The whole lot are a minefield. However, if it ***is*** *for a bit of cake...you put your left-arm in, your left-arm out, in out, in out, you shake it all about, you do the Okey Cokey and you turn around...I'll have another slice!*

Chapter 32 – Christmas 1978

December 1978

It was always hard for Rex to put his finger on exactly why Christmas 1978 went so wrong, but on reflection, maybe there were some clues. It wasn't Christmas Day itself, more the entire month of December that seemed unsettled.

Lucy wasn't particularly thrilled when Rex came home in late November, excitedly announcing that he was going to Germany for another six weeks. Somehow the enthusiasm simply wasn't there. Maybe that set the mood for the following month.

December seemed to start well enough when Helen gave birth to a bouncing baby boy named James. Lucy went to the hospital to offer her support during the birth, and both she and Helen cried tears of joy as young James popped into the world. That seemed to be a happy event.

Rex had a similar life-changing moment in 1978, which made him feel equally emotional. Only 12 months prior, his Christmas Day gluttony had been defeated by the mountain of icing sugar on top of Maureen's home made mince pies. As he took his first bite, he mistakenly inhaled some of the powdered sugar. The dramatic sneezing fit that followed left Maureen dismayed and Lucy crying with laughter. This year, Rex had a score to settle.

After the Queen's speech, Rex took two of Maureen's finest, scraped off the icing sugar, drowned them in custard and then scoffed the lot! That certainly taught them who was the boss.

For a Christmas gift, Rex had bought Lucy a brand-new stereo. It did of course have all the latest features but still needed a very thorough checking for faults by testing it repeatedly with *The Dark Side of the Moon*. Rex called it quality control.

On the 28th of December, Lucy celebrated her 24th birthday, which again was a happy enough day. Everyone in the Roman and Doggitt households still felt bloated from three days of excessive gorging on turkey, mince pies and Quality Street. As a result, four bodies were feeling too stuffed to move; all pledging that the diets would start in the New Year. Despite the indigestion and keen to beat the January deadline, Maureen, Peter, Rex and Lucy all jumped at the offer of a *free* slap-up birthday meal, organised and paid for by Crispin. No one turns down a freebie, do they?

Crispin had grown to know Lucy well during the last two years. The whole evening was his gift to her and a fabulous time was had by all. Rex sensibly stayed off of the alcohol, as he had done for some time.

Much to the delight of Rex, Maureen had ordered Lucy a surprise cake. A waitress brought the cake, complete with burning candles, over to the table while the whole restaurant sang Happy Birthday. Crispin made a fine speech about his wonderful friends, and everyone present was touched by his generosity and thoughtfulness in arranging the evening.

So that's the second time that Lucy burst into tears of joy during December 1978.

The other memorable moment was when another of Lucy's childhood friends came over to celebrate New Years Eve. Vicky burst into the house excitedly waving her left-hand in front of Lucy. Following behind and looking all pleased with himself was her boyfriend, Alan.

'Lucy, Lucy, look what Alan gave me for Christmas!'

'Oh my God!!!' screamed Lucy as the girls hugged and danced around the hall in circles.

Rex couldn't understand what the big fuss was all about. It was only a ring with a tiny diamond in the middle. What on earth could you do with it anyway? Confused thoughts ran through his mind…
'Er guys…hello…check out the stereo the size of a small house in the lounge. That's a proper present!'

Thankfully, he didn't vocalise his thoughts.

So there we have it. Three separate times when Lucy burst into tears of joy and happiness during December. So why on earth did she seem to be so unhappy for the rest of the month? Something was up, but Rex couldn't seem to quite put his finger on it. He trusted Lucy totally, so his mind was at rest, but there was a vibe that left a certain unease in the air.

With Christmas over, the tree disposed of and the decorations back in the loft, Rex, Lucy and Twinky were ready for all that 1979 had to offer. For a couple of weeks everything seemed really settled in the Roman household, until it was time for Rex to leave for Germany again...

* * *

(At this point, the more intuitive female readers have already spotted the problems brewing in the relationship.

The male readers are of course wondering what type of cake was eaten in the restaurant: Chocolate or vanilla sponge???

This is all part of the eternal struggle between the male and female minds.)

Chapter 33 – Es Ist Kalt

Jan - Mar 1979

It was in January 1979, that Rex had a further opportunity to expand his vegetable-based German vocabulary.

Thomas Mueller was working as an acting coach on a filmset in Berlin. Crispin decided this would be an ideal situation for Rex to learn about the complex art of film making.

Crispin had proven his worth as a well-connected agent, and his dealings with Rex often went well beyond those of a normal agent/client relationship. It was in truth a friendship, one that cost 15% of all earnings, but a friendship nonetheless.

Some actors work exclusively in theatres, some only seem to appear on television, yet most of them aspire to star on the big screen. The reality is that all three are totally different mediums. Very rarely do actors, or actresses, progress to a high profile movie career until they have paid their dues and learnt their craft.

Rex had been working steadily for the last few years, which was fairly unusual considering the low employment rate of the acting profession. Unfortunately, this blossoming career came at a cost. The lack of free time meant that Rex had ceased his martial arts training, only one year after he had finally achieved the coveted black belt status. As Rex set off on the path to his dreams, Steve Brown wished him luck with an appropriate quote from Confucius:

"Choose a job you love,
and you will never have to work a day in your life" *

*Copyright © Confucius Corporation 498BC. All rights reserved. Shaolin monks are watching.

Although Rex was hesitant about leaving Lucy for another six weeks, he recognised that opportunities to be on a filmset were hard to come by. He had to take this trip overseas if he was serious about learning. Rex didn't have any acting roles in the film, as such. He was there to learn from the other actors, the director and all the other highly skilled personnel that make up the crew on a location shoot. Sometimes the best way to learn is to just sit and watch.

Thomas had arranged for Rex to appear as a non-speaking extra in a few of the scenes, which in itself was really exciting.

If any of the scenes involved one of the cast shouting:

'Does anyone have a potato?'

Rex would be elevated to his first speaking role in a movie, based on his potato related vocal expertise, but he didn't hold out too much hope of that.

The synopsis of the film read like this:

Auf der Flucht

Missverstaendlich wird nach Klaus Schulz als Moerder gesucht. Um seine Unschuld zu beweisen, nimmt Schultz auf der Flucht vor den Behoerden die Ferte des wirklichen Taeters auf. Nachdem ihn die Spur des Moerders in einen Zirkus fuehrt, findet er dort mehr als er erwartet.

Naturally such a plot required most of the scenes to be shot in a giant circus tent, which had been constructed on the barren wasteland of Festplatz* in West Berlin.
('Festival place' or fairground. It was basically a circus tent in a field.*)

If you ever go to Berlin in January, then you may well learn a few things from your trip. One of them is that it's bitterly cold at that time of the year. Your brain will feel like it's freezing in your head if you don't wear a hat, so be prepared. Another is that you will learn to love coffee.

Nowadays, the modern coffee menu is a festival of choice. You can order: latte, mocha, espresso or maybe even a caramel macchiato if you are full of wild abandon. Adding chocolate sprinkles can be taking it a bit too far into the realms of dessert, but this is a sign of our liberal times. In 1979, if it was hot, wet and in a cup, then that was good enough.

Tea is the drink of choice in Britain, but in Berlin, Rex got a serious taste for coffee. Shivering in the catering area on set, huddled around a coffee pot with his thespian brothers, Rex learnt another important German phrase…

'Es ist kalt' ***(It is cold)***

The only possible answer to this was a resounding ***"JA"***, and therefore Rex was once again making friends and influencing people.

Even more friends were made when some extra crew were flown in from England. Away from Britain you miss your language, so it was good to hear all of the news from back home coming from native residents. One particular production manager named Dick, was a dab hand with a packet of biscuits, so he and Rex instantly had a mutual respect for one another.

Although Dick was appalled by the health and safety risks of a few of the tent pegs and the chaotic layout of the site, he seemed to be at home wading through a muddy field. He and Rex were happiest in the catering area of the set where a few games of cards, combined with some serious biscuit-dunking sessions, made for a strong bond.

Many people involved in the arts have creative personalities. Sometimes this creativity is labelled *eccentric* or more routinely *plain madness*. It is fair to say that for a few of the actors on set, *their cheese had well and truly slid off of their crackers*, but overall the cast seemed very professional.

The director of the film was Frederick Hunzelbergerstraum. A snappy dressing bear of a man, Frederick strode around the set like he owned the place. This attitude was thoroughly appropriate because on a filmset, the director is always the king of all he surveys.

Frederick was a friendly, highly intelligent man, and Rex got chatting to him over lunch one day…

'So you must be der Englander friend of Thomas, ja? I am director of ze film - Frederick Hunzelbergerstraum.'

Rex didn't know if 'sir' was the customary word for a German gentleman. Acting on some language advice he had received from Thomas, he tried to say the following in English...

"Yes, my name is Rex Roman. Pleased to meet you **Herr** Hunzelbergerstraum". Rex got as far as… *"Yes, my name is Rex Roman..."* then the rest of the sentence descended into linguistic chaos. The *"pleased to meet you..."* was okay, if slightly hesitant, but the *"Herr Hunzelbergerstraum"* was a bloodbath.

Rex had real problems pronouncing the director's name.

Many words in the German vocabulary are extremely long and vocally challenging. As Rex had chosen to study French rather than German at Winston school, he was struggling.

'I see you do not speak German, do you Rex?'

'No, Hair Hands and Burger Room.'

Another battle lost!

'Please stop, please, I can't bear it,' cried Frederick, wincing in pain at the verbal mutilation of his fine German name.

'Rex, Thomas tells me you are good friend and talented actor. In film, it always is good to make many friends as you can. Maybe one day, I vill direct one of your films, so today I vill make you favour.'

Rex was embarrassed yet surprised by the offer…

'So, vill you like to call me Herman?'

'Oh, yes please,' replied Rex, nodding profusely.

'I know you Englanders sink it is highly amusing to call us all *Herman ze German.'*

Rex chuckled.

'Ja, ja...you Englanders are so sophisticated viz your humour.'

'How about Mr Herman?' said Rex, offering a seemingly more respectful solution.

'Mr Herman it is. I like it.'

Deal!!! The pair shook hands, and for the next six weeks, the genial Mr Herman taught Rex all about the art of film making. Camera angles, lighting and sound recording all proved enthralling topics of conversation for Rex as he discussed them at length with both Thomas and Herman. Each technique was an art in its own right, and a technician was on hand for every probability.

Because Rex didn't understand the dialogue, he didn't learn much from the script, so he made a point of closely studying all the actors for their body language and eye movements. He soon noticed that both of these elements made a world of difference to the quality of the acting, and he would utilise these technical skills in his own career. Luckily, his next role back home was playing Zebedee, in a stage adaptation of the popular children's teatime show - *The Magic Roundabout*. The good people of Hemel Hempstead were in for a treat!

Life on a filmset was vastly different to treading the boards in small regional theatres, and Rex loved watching the whole process of film making, amazed at the amount of technical equipment and sheer numbers of personnel involved. He knew that if he paid his dues, this was where he could be in the future; a main actor in the cast of a movie.

Rex did actually appear in the film, as a non-speaking extra, and if you ever get the chance to see the 1979, classic thriller *Auf der Flucht* directed by Mr Herman the German - then you should definitely take it!

* * *

With the filming completed and the tent dismantled, leaving a right old mess in the field that 'Bomber' Harris would have been proud of, the film crew moved on. Rex moved back to London, inspired by his trip.

When Lucy collected Rex from Heathrow airport, he didn't receive the same ecstatic welcome he had enjoyed some two years earlier. Maybe as they were living together, the novelty had worn off? Whatever it was, it seemed that some of the earlier gloom, so obvious in December, had returned to create a tense atmosphere.

On the journey home, Rex was questioned about why he hadn't made more phone calls back to England. He was then accused of living a glamorous lifestyle and forgetting all about what really mattered. Rex explained that he had actually been freezing in a circus tent for most of the time, surrounded by some less than fragrant crew, slightly more fragrant elephants, two rogue ducks and even a bearded lady at one point. As there were no payphones in the field or the near-by area, it was impossible to ring back home. The mobile phone was still a distant piece of technology waaayyy back then, so his reasons were valid. Lucy didn't seem that mightily impressed by the excuses at first but eventually abandoned her enquiries.

Twinky was so thrilled to see Daddy that she merrily hopped between both her high and low perches in celebration. If only Lucy had been as happy to see him as that budgie was.

For Rex, looking back, this trip was probably the point where his relationship with Lucy started to take a turn for the worse.

Chapter 34 – Professor Plum

Sunday 2nd December 1979

Having spent most of 1979, taking any job he could get, Rex was finding that he had a few chickens coming home to roost. Those earlier egg laying sessions with Crispin were finally hatching into professional paid work.

Rex would take any part, no matter how small. Unconventional theatre productions and the wacky world of advertising had all benefited from his acting talents, in one form or another. Rex had no shame; he was shameless in his desire to establish a real career and to make Lucy proud of him.

Lucy didn't seem that proud or pleased though when Rex announced he was starring as Professor Plum, in a unique touring production of the ever popular board game - *Cluedo.*

Rex had a real dilemma on his hands. He wanted to take the role, but the final date was on Saturday 1st of December in Bolton, in the northern part of England.

Lucy was upset about this, swiftly pointing out that this date would be the evening of their 5th anniversary. She wanted them to be together for this special occasion.

Rex countered with the promise that he would be home on Sunday the 2nd, the following day. If he caught an early train he would be back by midday to spoil her like a princess in celebration of five wonderful years together.

Lucy still didn't seem that impressed.

Meanwhile... Helen, Martin and the baby were all doing well, with young James coming up to his first birthday. Vicky had married Alan in the September of 1979, but Rex was unable to attend the wedding due to his work commitments. He'd heard that it had been a great bash and his humorous dancing skills were sorely missed.

Maureen and Peter had married when they were both just 19-years-old. Despite some negative people saying that it would never last, this year had seen them happily celebrate their 26th wedding anniversary. At the celebration meal with the whole family present, Rex felt secure enough in his relationship to eat half his bodyweight in garlic bread. Cleverly spotting the danger, he avoided the wine.

Twinky was going from strength to strength and had finally mastered the art of watching television on Daddy's shoulder. She didn't do the mad dash thing like Stanley did when she came out to play. Instead, Rex would put his index finger into the cage, and she would step onto it, ready to be escorted to the couch. She was a little diva really.

Bradley, Roy and Kate were all keeping in touch via the miracle of long distance phone calls. Regular, weekly chats saved the friendships and seemed to shorten the distance. It was a bit strange talking to people in a time-zone eight hours behind London, but somehow, with a bit of pre-planning, the schedules worked. Rex and Lucy hadn't found the time to visit America yet, but the money was still safe in the jam jar. They would go when they could.

So there we have it, a summary of 1979, so far. There were lots of memorable moments really, with an anniversary, a wedding and a best friend's baby all keeping Lucy happy. Life was all going along very nicely indeed - *Except, now we go...*

Back to the Plum dilemma... Crispin had been highly instrumental in securing Rex the prestigious Professor Plum role. By now though, he was much more than an agent. He was actually more of a father figure, filling the vacant position previously and scarily held by Roy. The father figure was a good-looking chap, so Rex had renamed him *"Mr Handsome"* disposing of the correct greeting of *Mr Hansen*. Rex thought that this play on words was hilarious, and Crispin took to it with surprising ease. He was a bit vain, so such flattery played well to his ego.

Lucy had pointed out, two days before Rex left for his tour, that she was going to be 25-years-old just after Christmas. As a result, she felt that her biological clock was ticking. Rex burst into song, accompanied by his air guitar, with: *"ticking away, the moments that make up a dull day"* at her serious comment. Lucy, once again, didn't seem to be too happy.

Rex couldn't understand why she got so upset because he knew that she loved Pink Floyd just as much as he did. He mistakenly thought that his impromptu performance of **Time** would make her forget her mid-twenties crisis.

Everything seemed settled though by the time Rex left for his four week jaunt with the wicked Miss Scarlett, dastardly Colonel Mustard and the other scoundrels of the cast. The play was a triumph and Aimee Thomas of the Grimsby Gazette described Rex as: "the finest Plum ever to grace Grimsby".

With the tour concluded, Rex looked forward to returning home. The train ride from Bolton to London was a long one, but as today was his belated anniversary, this gave Rex a good opportunity to plan the rest of the day. His schedule went like this...

Pssst...it's over there... 

Rex & Lucy's 5yr Anniversary List

~~1st~~ 2nd Dec 1979

Home between 11.30am – Noon:
with ~~hot dogs,~~ bunch of flowers, box of chocolates

Make Lucy some toasted bacon sandwiches
(ADD lashings of tomato ketchup)
all served with a cup of tea and extra love

2pm: Go for a long walk together
buy Sunday papers

Come home, read papers, snuggle up, listen to
NEW Pink Floyd album – The Wall

5-7pm: Listen to the Top 40 on Radio 1 while
cooking Lucy full roast chicken dinner wearing
the silly apron she bought me

7pm onwards: Eat and then Daddy settles
down with the girls for some television action

Rex you are one smooth operator!!!!!!!!!!!!

It all sounded perfect. Lucy would be happy with such a romantic schedule, and maybe they could get the Christmas decorations out too, if there was time.

Pink Floyd had recently released a new album, *The Wall,* and Rex had a brand-new copy. He hadn't even removed the shrink-wrap yet as he was looking to share his first-ever listen with Lucy. It would only make their special day that much more memorable.

Walking down the street carrying some fresh flowers, a small holdall and a box of Milk Tray chocolates, Rex could barely wait to see his beautiful girlfriend.

Putting the key into the front door and entering the house, this was going to be quite a reunion…

Chapter 35 – Two Lost Souls

Sunday 2nd December 1979

'Honey, I'm home!' shouted Rex, taking his key out of the front door, excitedly entering the lounge.

Rex couldn't quite put his finger on it, but something was different about the atmosphere in the house. Something was missing.

'Why does the house feel so empty? Where's Twinky?'

That was it. That's what was missing. The golden ray of feathered sunshine that would sing so merrily whenever Daddy came in was not singing today.

'Lucy must have taken her to Maureen's, so we can have some quality alone-time. She'll be back soon. Hmmm…I'm really thirsty.'

Carefully placing the chocolates on top of the gigantic stereo and throwing his festering holdall back into the hall, Rex went into the kitchen to get a vase for the flowers.

Normally, the first thing that Rex does when he gets home is turn on the kettle for a cup of tea, before he raids the biscuit tin for an accompanying snack. This time, the hunt for a custard cream or two had been suspended as the search for a vase was stepped up. Suddenly, he noticed a hand written envelope that had been carefully placed next to the kettle.

Rex dropped the flowers and stared in horror at the letter. His hand was shaking as he went to pick it up. Once he had the courage to open the envelope, the note inside read…

Dearest Rex,

I have always loved you and will always love you.

From the moment I saw you I wanted to be with you, so I squirted you with ketchup...on purpose!

Sorry about that

I don't regret it though as the past five years have been wonderful, but sadly I feel our time together is over.

Now that you are following your dreams, I am constantly alone and I miss you all the time.

I need change - I want marriage and children.
I can't explain why I feel this way, but if I stay, I will only hold you back. I want you to succeed and for you to do that - you need to be free.
This is the right thing to do, for the both of us.

I love you too much to stay friends, so I beg of you, please let me go.

Remember me when you're famous.
I will never forget you.

Lucy
xXx

Rex's heart broke right there on the spot. He stumbled to the sofa, buried his head in his hands and cried like a baby.

After an hour of blind panic, he composed himself and started thinking...

'Maureen's!...she'll be at Maureen's. Okay, all I have to do is go round there and beg her to come back. We can work it out, we have to. I'm nothing without her.'

Rex soon arrived at Maureen's and knocked on the front door, his hand shaking from the stress.

'Hello Maureen...is Lucy there?'

Maureen could tell that Rex had been crying and felt real sympathy for him, but no matter how much she too loved Rex, she loved her own daughter more.

'Oh Rex, I am so sorry. Lucy is in France. She told me she was going to do this. I tried to talk her out of it, but you know how determined she can be once she's made her mind up about something.'

Rex knew this for sure, and his heart sank. Lucy didn't suffer from the same indecisiveness that made his every decision such an extended drama. She was sensible; she was a lateral thinker. Rex knew at that moment, he was facing a whole new world...alone.

It turned out that Lucy had gone to her grandmother's house in France, and the rest of the family were going to join her there for Christmas. She needed time to heal from the split. She was not with anyone else, but she was not coming back to Rex.

When he returned home, Rex discovered a few surprises dotted around the house. Lucy had left a note…

'I love you Rex, I will never forget you' on his pillow.

She had left some PBJ sandwiches in the fridge, with a note attached…

'Eat me, go on you know you want me'

The house had been hoovered, cleaned throughout and fresh sheets were on the bed. Everything was perfect for Rex to come home to after his long tour. The money was still in the jam jar, and if Lucy had found the bread pudding recipe, she probably would have made some of that, too.

Rex had to adjust to a whole new way of life. He would have to accept that Lucy was never again going to come in through the front door.

This was a chapter in his life, Rex never wanted to write.

Chapter 36 – Swimming In A Fish Bowl

25th - 31st December 1979

Christmas is a time for celebration, family, friends, joy and goodwill to all mankind no matter what colour, creed or religion. The world always seems to be a better place on this one special day of the year.

However, when you are without the one you love and you spend Christmas Day on your own, it can only serve to highlight your sadness, misery and loneliness.

Rex was too sad to spend the day with Crispin, even though the offer was there. Rex was too sad to do anything much. Without Lucy there was no point in putting a tree up. She always made it look so pretty; there was no way Rex could hope to match it, so he didn't even try. Having totally lost his appetite for food, Christmas Day lunch consisted of three slices of toast with baked beans on the side of the plate.

Rex was a shadow of the happy, creative man he had been just one month earlier. While he was on the stage performing, bringing the house down with his *"more tea, vicar?"* gags as he offered Reverend Green a beverage, his loving girlfriend was at home waiting for him to return.

That was the problem, Rex spent time away performing while Lucy spent time at home waiting. The separation was destructive, and Rex had totally failed to see the growing disconnection. He didn't mean to. He loved Lucy dearly and wanted to be with her, but the nature of his career meant the hours were irregular. It was a lifestyle more than a career.

Rex Roman is not stupid. It's simply a character flaw that he fails to spot the obvious sometimes, there is no malice there. If only Lucy had said directly how unhappy she was and explained it, then Rex would have known about the problems. He would have done something to change, but in Rex World everything seemed fine in the relationship.

It was 1979, and Britain was in a desperate state of affairs. Times were really hard.

The only real mild disagreements Rex and Lucy had were usually about whose turn it was to make the tea or who was changing the television channel. In those days, to change a TV channel you were forced to get up from the comfort of the sofa, walk all the way over to the television set, physically push a button and then trudge all the way back, only to realise the new programme was rubbish, just as you sat down again. As you can imagine, in 1979, times were really hard.

Lucy loved Rex; he was an actor, and she was proud of him. As Rex was constantly struggling to balance his career and his personal life, Lucy wanted to set him free of his inner conflict. In her mind, once she had left, Rex would go on to achieve even greater success. In some ways her action was both selfless and noble. It was also the worst thing she could have done.

Lucy may have felt that she was holding Rex back, but in truth, she was the one that was inspiring him to go forwards. She was fanning the fire in his belly with her love and support. Before he met her, yes he had a dream, but he was happy to just sit around with Bradley and Nan, talking nonsense and watching the world go by. Sometimes it is better to dream the dream than it is to achieve it.

A life without Lucy?...well the fire that was burning brightly, wasn't burning quite so brightly anymore.

Every morning was the same; Rex would wake up in a soaking wet bed. He would get so anxious during the night that he would sweat during terrible panic attacks, caused by fear for what his future held. Every day he would change the sheets, and every night he would panic.

Rex missed everything about Lucy. Her company, her beauty, her smell, her clothes in the cupboard and strangely, her mess in the bathroom. He even missed not hearing little Twinky singing away as she swung in her cage. The whole house felt cold and empty without the girls, it was all too painful to comprehend.

At about 5pm the phone rang. Rex hoped for a miracle…

'Oh, thank God. It's Lucy…she's coming back! Let's forget all about this and live happily ever after. Let's get married, have children and do whatever it takes to stay together. Just stay, please, please stay... C'mon Rex, this is it...tell her how you feel.'

'Hello. Lu-'

'MERRY CHRISTMAS!!!'

It wasn't Lucy. It was Bradley ringing from Los Angeles. The Milwee family were awake and calling to extend their seasons greetings.

Sigh!…'Merry Christmas.'

'Rex! My God, what's wrong?'

When people know you, it's amazing how just two words can instantly say so much. If those two words happen to be *"Merry Christmas"* and they can tell you are in crisis; they really do know you very well indeed.

'It's Lucy…she's gone.'

Rex broke down in tears, as he had done on many occasions during the previous three weeks. Somehow, having Bradley on the phone meant that he could let it all out.

Bradley obviously said something at home as all of a sudden, Kate came to the rescue.

'Rex honey, what's wrong?…what's happened?'

If there is one thing you have got to love about Kate Milwee, it's her voice. That woman could soothe a raging bull into attending a tea party. Once there, it would stop raging, put on a napkin, sit quietly and probably even pass the sugar. Kate had a voice that could always soothe Rex when he was anxious. She was a Mom and a great one, too. Rex was another one of her boys.

As Rex stayed on the phone for over an hour, he explained everything the way he saw it and wondered why Lucy had left him. Kate gave the woman's perspective, and at the end of the conversation, Rex felt no anger towards Lucy, he never had. In some ways he felt glad she had left. Glad she had left for herself.

Was Rex really ready to get married straight away? No, he wasn't. He had an issue with it, having seen his parents fight so badly as a child. He had also been trapped in an unhappy home of conflict throughout his youth, so he wasn't at all convinced that marriage was right for him.

Was Rex ready to have children and all the responsibilities that go with them, both emotionally and financially? Not really. The man still needed to grow-up himself. He had a child-like spirit best expressed through a nomadic, artistic career. This demanding profession often kept him away from home and meant that children were not an option at this time.

Rex loved Lucy so much, he only wanted her to be happy. She deserved to have a companion who could always be by her side and end the constant loneliness. Could Rex really take another five years of Lucy's life from her, following **his** dream? No he couldn't, that would be too selfish.

In time, Lucy would surely marry someone else and finally get rid of that awful surname. Some lucky man would have a family with her, and if he had any sense, he would never, ever let her go.

When Bradley came back on the phone, he had already hatched a plan.

'Dude, come and live here. Make a fresh start.'

Wow! This was a huge statement; one that took Rex completely by surprise.

'Live there??? What with you and your parents?'

'Good grief no! No, I've been talking to Roy while you were on the phone with Mom. He knows of a cool two-bed rental apartment in North Hollywood. He says that if you come here, he'll pay the first six months rent for us, just to get me out of the house.'

'Really?' Rex couldn't believe this. Only a couple of hours before it had seemed as though his world had ended, but now there was fresh hope.

'Yeah, come on, man. We live out in Calabasas. I'm twenty miles out from where I want to be. I wanna be in the centre, where the action is.'

'Well, I don't know.'

'Come on, it'll be fun. Come out for the winter at least. You know the sun shines here most days, right? You'll love it.'

Two simple things to remember about Rex Roman:

One: He hates the winters in England. With all the cold weather, grey skies and short daylight hours, he just feels that he's trapped in darkness. It's a long slog until March when the clocks go forward and spring finally arrives.

Two: If you give him an idea it will sit there in his mind, being analysed and digested from every conceivable angle. If it's good, it will rapidly grow and he will get excited about the possibilities. If it's bad, it will get shredded immediately. This one from Bradley was a grower.

'Can I think about it? Let me talk to CH about a few things.'

'Sure. I'll call you Monday to wish you Happy New Year. Let me know then, okay?'

'Alright, mate. I will…and Bradley…thanks for being a friend.'

'Friends forever, buddy. You know that.'

Rex came off the phone and spent the rest of Christmas Day making his lists, as he did, working out the pros and cons of moving overseas. As he sat alone in the house for the next few days, he went through pages and pages of notes, list after list after list.

Now many, if not all, of our female readers are probably delighted that Lucy left Rex, and they too would have left him the moment they saw his twiglet legs and truly terrible pant collection. But ladies please be gentle, for over the period between Christmas and the New Year, Rex did some serious soul searching.

Rex realised the error of his ways. His shame was no secret - it was overwhelming. He became riddled with guilt over the things he didn't do or didn't say and that he would never again have the opportunity to put right. He recognised where he went wrong. He spent hours reliving the wonderful times he and Lucy had shared together: how they met, her awesome slow-motion fighting and her infectious giggle. Rex began to recognise all she had done for him in the name of love. He had been so busy following his career that he had taken his eye off of the prize at home. He had taken Lucy's love for granted believing that it would always be there, and he had made a big mistake. Everyone makes mistakes at some point in their life, don't they?

Yet, rather than try and beg Lucy to come back with promises of change, Rex decided that the best thing for Lucy was to let her go. Someone so precious should not be held back by **his** career dreams. She must be allowed to spread her wings and fly away. Rex was thankful that he had even felt so much love, so deeply and for so long. He would always know what true love felt like and the power that it brought to his soul.

Rex was about to take the pain, no matter how intense, to ensure that Lucy could start her new life with a clean break. This was at least the decent thing to do. He could not put right the past, but he could do something about the future. Remembering his dear old Nan, Rex could hear her say…

"If you love someone then set them free.
If they come back, then it was meant to be."

* * *

(**Please Note:** This book is a limited edition due to absolutely zero demand. Therefore, this page is your Certificate of Authentication and only appears in the original, first print run. We know what you're thinking…*'great…I'll sell it on eBay and double my money'* **but hold on!!!** This is a collector's copy **so keep it.** Sadly, in future copies, the fun may be further diluted by some more spineless lawyers. Ah well! On the plus side though, the text will all be proof read by someone who understands grammar and knows how to use a spell checka. Frankly, we haven't got a clue, so please don't write in and complain about comma's in the wrong, places. The full and final release of the book should be shrink-wrapped with a sticker on the front like so…)

NOW in proper English

Includes
FREE Kung Fu poster
FREE Rex sticker
FREE Rexasaurus

Note:
The Dark Side of the Moon was originally shrink-wrapped with 2 stickers and 2 posters thrown in FREE. Everyone likes a bit of value so who could possibly resist a free copy of the glorious Kung Fu poster in a future edition?

No doubt some bean counter will dismiss it as too expensive to produce, but it's a lovely idea.

Anyway, back to the story…

Crispin was not too surprised to hear that Rex was thinking about moving to Los Angeles. As expected, his contacts book extended to international dialling, and he believed that Rex could probably pick up some work over there.

1980 was all about a fresh start, and Rex was going to embrace that ideal.

Initially Rex wanted to sell his house, leave all his possessions and run away. Crispin and his lawyer, Ben, suggested Rex should take some time to think it all through. If there was to be a fast getaway, then selling would only slow his escape. Rex just wanted to go quickly, so he took their wise advice.

More time spent alone in the house simply confirmed that without Lucy, this was no longer a home. Everywhere Rex went, he could see her. Every time he saw her, his heart ached, longing to have her back.

In the end, it was decided that the house should be left for Crispin to take care of. That way, Rex would still have a place in London so that whenever he came back, he would have somewhere to live. If it was being rented, then he would stay with Crispin until the tenants left. It all seemed to make perfect sense. After six days of looking at every single conceivable scenario, Rex told Bradley his decision…

'I'll do it!'

'Excellent! You're gonna love it here, dude.'

'I'll book a flight next week. I've still got the money your Dad gave me.'

'Cool! Let me know the arrival time, and I'll come and collect you from LAX myself…this is fantastic news. I can't wait to see you again.'

The decision was made, so now it was time to execute the plan. Roy and Bradley would sort out the new apartment; Rex would pack up his belongings and make arrangements to leave London. With thousands of miles of land and ocean between Rex and his love, somehow the sense of loss would be easier to deal with.

Rex Roman was about to leave his home country, and he was never going to return - EVER!

Goodbye Lucy my love
Please take care and be happy
Rex
x

Chapter 37 – Rex In LA

Wednesday 6th February 1980

Los Angeles, USA, always has been and probably always will be, the home of film and television entertainment...we're talking about Hollywood, baby!

It is every aspiring actor's ambition to be located there, in the thick of the action. All those with a dream have countless opportunities to practise their *Schmooze* and *Embellishment* skills. After all, LA invented such dark arts in the first place. If you are hungry for stardom, you go there.

Alternatively, if you are so sad, lonely and miserable that you long for the company and the friendship of people that care about you...well, that's a valid reason to go there, too.

Los Angeles is a vast city, much bigger than London, and the area of North Hollywood is a good location for both actors and musicians. For those on the up, this area offers a large collection of drama, rehearsal and recording studios, plus other entertainment related facilities.

For the working actors, Burbank is right next to North Hollywood and is home to NBC television as well as many studio lots. For the established stars, at the top of the business, the mansions in the Hollywood Hills are only a short drive away.

Rex wasn't in the right frame of mind to think about his career anymore. Acting and show business, with all of its smoke and mirrors, simply didn't matter. Lucy was all that really mattered. She was real, but she was gone.

True to Roy's word, Bradley and Rex were now living in a very comfortable, two-bedroom apartment in Kling Street, *(off the main road - Vine Street)* North Hollywood.

Rex had only recently arrived and was feeling pretty sorry for himself. He hadn't even seen Roy or Kate yet as he just didn't feel up to it. He would see them soon, but right now everyone was giving him the time and space to recover. They had known him this distraught before, when Nan died, and they had faith that he would come out of it eventually.

It's worth mentioning that the only worthwhile thing Rex had done since arriving in Los Angeles, was solve *"the great Marathon mystery"*. The Marathon chocolate bar, much to Rex's annoyance, had been renamed Snickers in the UK. The exact same six-inch, peanut packed, chocolate, caramel and nougat treat was sold as a Snickers in the USA. Therefore, the UK name change was all part of a global branding exercise on behalf of the manufacturers.

This was how Rex filled his day. It was pathetic.

It was nearly six o'clock, when the early evening gloom in the apartment was disturbed by a loud ringing sound. Rex picked up the intercom phone by the sofa…

'Hello.'

'Hey dude, it's me, can you buzz me in?'

It was Bradley returning home from work. After a day spent watching television, Rex was ready for some company.

What happened next is not for the faint-hearted…

Bradley walked into the lounge dressed as a 6-foot chicken, maybe 6-foot, 4-inches if you include the impressive red crown. He grabbed himself a cold one from the fridge and sat on the sofa, as any giant, feathered bird would do after a hard day at the office.

'What's on?' asked Bradley, taking a chug on his beer, staring at the telly.

'Bradley…I can't help but notice that you're dressed as a rather large chicken.'

'What this?...yeah, I hate my job…I'm working for Frank's Fast Food down near Sunset. This is all part of Frank's idea to get more business.'

'How is that exactly?' enquired Rex, curious to know more about this marketing plan.

'I get to walk around outside the joint, with my giant chicken presence, trying to entice customers inside to sample the food Frank has on special offer.'

'Ah, I see. Living the dream,' said Rex. It all made sense.

'Actually I am. Today was my last day working in the crazy world of poultry for a while. As from tomorrow, I am working on the Pink Floyd show at the Memorial Sports Arena.'

This newsflash lifted Rex from his couch potato slouch.

'You're working with Pink Floyd? Bradley, I am so impressed. How on earth did you manage that?'

This truly was incredible, no sensational, news. Rex tried to digest it…

'Bradley did say he wanted to get his music going again when he left for the States. He always was a great guitar player, and now he's playing with Pink Floyd? This is mind-blowing!'

Then, the truth started to emerge…'Well…I'm not *in* the band exactly, more working *for* the band. I shall be lending my unique talents to the show to make sure everything is perfect…for YOU!'

With this, Bradley produced two concert tickets that had been cleverly concealed in a neat little pouch under his wing.

'Blimey! How did you get these?' asked Rex, impressed by the tickets and the natty little pouch.

'This is LA, my home town. I have contacts here now.'

'Bradley, you are a genius!'

'A red-crowned, yellow-feathered, big-footed genius, if you don't mind.'

Rex thought long and hard as he sat on the sofa staring at the tickets. If someone helped him out in life, he always felt obliged to return the favour.

'You know, Bradley. If you ever need help with the whole chicken thing, I've got some good moves I can show you. I learnt them in Germany a few years ago.'

Rex watched the television, while Bradley drank his beer. Here they were: Oscar the Grouch and Big Bird having a lads' night in. One was grumpy; the other was burping - but at least they were together…again.

Chapter 38 – The Feast

Saturday 9th February 1980

It was the morning of the Pink Floyd concert when Rex decided to dig out his copy of *The Wall*.

Bradley was out of the apartment, running some errands before he had to go to work. Rex felt that he should listen to the band's latest album before the show. The whole concert was based on this one record, so to ensure he could sing along, Rex had some studying to do.

Having put the album away for the last couple of months, on account of the emotional trauma he associated with it, Rex really wasn't that familiar with *The Wall*. He had been hoping to listen to it for the first time with Lucy, when he returned from his Professor Plum tour, but this was sadly not to be.

The album was riding high in the charts, and just two months prior, **Another Brick in the Wall** had captured the imagination of every school kid in Britain. Their pocket money had been well spent as this single became the Christmas Number One for 1979. Not known for their singles, Pink Floyd are widely considered to be an albums band as the quality of their work is so consistently high, each whole album deserves your full attention.

For Rex, moving to Los Angeles was about moving on. It was also about a fresh start and an escape from the pain. Now that he had Bradley back in his life, it would be easier to adjust to an unfamiliar country. His friend's support was a great source of comfort to him as he tried to heal his broken heart.

The decision to play *The Wall* was about to save Rex's career.

Nearly three years prior, Rex had abandoned his glittering air guitar career, following the loss of Stanley. Such was his shame at 'losing' his fine feathered friend, Rex just couldn't bring himself to practise anymore - and retired.

Comfortably Numb was about to change all that.

Comfortably Numb contains probably one of the greatest guitar solos of all-time. It actually has not one but two solos that cannot fail to impress. 2 minutes and 5 seconds into the song, you arrive at the first guitar solo. A 40 second interlude, full of tasteful playing.

If music truly is the 'food of love', as William Shakespeare once wrote, then this first solo is the perfect starter to your meal. It is perhaps a prawn cocktail of a solo. Succulent shrimp topped in a thousand island dressing, sprinkled with a light dusting of cayenne pepper, all served on a bed of crisp lettuce and garnished with a lemon. Fresh brown bread is on the side, lightly buttered and cut into small triangles.

Delicious! Yet it is merely an appetiser for the behemoth of a guitar solo that is to follow some 90 seconds later. This solo truly is the Daddy! With nearly 2 minutes of face-contorting, heart-pumping, and string-bending fury, this is the stuff true Floyd fans the world over dream of.

This is the main course!!! Imagine the most succulent food you can: moist, juicy, tender, all prepared to perfection and served on a silver platter. Everything you could hope for is right there in front of your eyes. Go on, tuck in.

The beauty of this feast is that it contains no calories and you never, ever get full. As soon as you have finished the meal, you are free to gorge all over again.

That day, Rex ate like a pig. Bradley's record player, with its clever repeat function, had been set to extend the banquet and prolong the guitar practice. The seasoned veteran was back in the saddle, displaying his delightful touch on the detached Hoover handle, with the grace of a true rock star. Round and round the vinyl disc span as Rex was not only playing the solos - he was **in** the band!

Rick was laying down the Hammond organ. Nick and Roger were supplying the rhythm section, underpinning the sound. David was on rhythm guitar while Rex was on lead, teaching David a few hot licks and some interesting facial expressions. The boy was good. Some say it was the ultimate comeback gig. A legend was born.

It was probably as Rex had one foot on the coffee table, head tilted back to the ceiling, just coming to the end of yet another faultless performance, that he heard…

'Caught ya!'

As Rex sheepishly dropped his head and closed his gaping jaw, he saw Bradley leaning against the doorway. Having finished his morning's errands, he'd been watching in silent amusement as Rex and the boys did their thing. Not one to pass judgment, Bradley rushed into his bedroom and returned with a tennis racquet. Strange considering Bradley could actually play guitar and had the real article tucked under his bed, but then where was the fun in that? This was a bout of stupidity Bradley was only too eager to embrace.

As the record went round one more time, Pink Floyd had not one but two of the finest lead guitar players the world has ever known…in Kling Street, North Hollywood, anyway.
(David was trying his best on rhythm guitar.)

Bradley's choice of a short-handled tennis racquet certainly gave him excessive string possibilities, but it severely hampered his growling low notes. Such depth could only be found at the furthest end of the 'guitar' neck and Rex, with his extended Hoover handle, led the way in that department. He taught the young American pretender a thing or two about how it should be done, totally outshining him at times by fully utilising his immense length. This was a gunslingers duel, where two evenly matched exponents were locked in mortal combat, for the honour of rock.

Rex and Bradley had so much fun that morning, and for the first time in months, Rex felt good about life again. It was also a bonding time for their friendship; one that had so far endured 13 years of whatever life could throw at them.

David Gilmour saved Rex that day, and he probably doesn't even know it.

Thank you very much, sir.

* * *

Top Rex Tip 3: *Although the Gibson Les Brush is undoubtedly a fine instrument to assist your performance of Comfortably Numb, you really should consider the Fender Strato-Hoover. This light-weight, metal-bodied piece of art is far less likely to go out of tune and has a tone that you simply won't believe. Get the song on, get your Hoover handle out and fire it up. It's the only way to go.*

Photos from Rex's treasured musical equipment collection appear on the website that has been lamely thrown together over a latte, to support the magnificently low key release of this book. As you are one of the privileged few to have a first-edition copy, then you should surely savour the experience and log onto this website.

The website address is: **www.rexroman.com**

View the *Musical Legend* section, before the inevitable phone calls from the Hard Rock Cafe force us to consider selling the collection for the price of two free burgers and fries, possibly a couple of milk shakes if we really haggle.

Click and marvel at Rex's custom air Marshall amp. This beautiful piece of sonic perfection has NO volume knob at all. Its volume is permanently calibrated to 14, which gives him **three** more than any other young pretender on the planet. Amazing! *(No knob gags! - signed The Publisher)*

Once again, this page will be removed from the second print run, so you are witnessing history in the making. This is the magna carta of air guitar tips. A piece of literary history as yet unappreciated by a single literary agent, publisher, critic, book store, distribution company, wholesaler or indeed, any other respected author.

That's what makes this book so unique!!!

* * *

Note:
Fender, Gibson & Hoover currently have no plans to release any official Rex Roman guitar models…which is a shame :o(Luckily, some merchandising charlatan is no doubt feverishly mocking up a prototype.

Chapter 39 – The Wall Concert

Saturday 9th February 1980

You cannot possibly imagine the scale of Pink Floyd's *The Wall* concerts, unless you were lucky enough to see one. Such a huge concert had to be held in a suitably huge venue.

The Los Angeles Memorial Sports Arena was an appropriate choice.

Rex and Bradley had again obtained two tickets for the front row on Saturday night, courtesy of Roy. That man's contacts seemed to know no international borders; such was the vast expanse of the underworld. Rex didn't want to know how Roy got them, but he did want those tickets.

Inspired by some guitar duelling in the apartment earlier that day, Rex now felt ready for this. He was excited about music again for the first time in months.

On account of some work commitments, Bradley arranged to meet up with Rex at the concert. With two guaranteed seats in the bank, they would still sit together even if they didn't arrive together.

Naturally the timing of the evening was planned to allow sufficient merchandise selection, ambience soaking and of course - a hot dog snack. Rituals perfected at the Wembley shows in England, were easily transported across the pond to Los Angeles.

Now the Americans do love their hot dogs, and they also love a bit of razzmatazz. Those who say that the English seaside town of Blackpool is the 'Vegas of the North' have clearly never been to the real Las Vegas in Nevada. When the Americans sell something, they really sell it. Passion, showbiz, spectacle and enthusiasm; it's all there. Rex loves this about America. Even buying a hot dog is showbiz, and in 1980, in a sports arena in Los Angeles, it was no different.

Despite the size of the venue, Rex detected an oasis of flavour with his hot sausage sonar. The tractor beam of taste began reeling in its hapless victim with a delightful onion aroma when Rex noticed that stood in front of the stand, was a full length, 7-foot hot dog. This spectacular vision consisted of a complete rubber suit with two arms, two legs and a man inside devoted to selling the product...

'Hot Dogs, Hot Dogs, get 'em fresh, Hot Dogs!'

This was a sale. This was how it should be sold, with passion. As Rex got closer, his look of joy turned to one of total horror.

'BRADLEY???' Rex could barely believe his eyes.

'Hey dude...come on, I caught you this morning...so...now I guess we're even.'

'I thought you were working on the show?' said Rex, unable to comprehend why his childhood friend was stood in front of him dressed as a giant, but altogether delicious, snack.

'I am working! You don't think I'd wear this for fun do you?'

Good point.

Once the shock had worn off, Rex got his hot dog with onions while Bradley continued the hard sell.

'Don't be late,' ordered Rex as he left to take up his ambience soaking position in the front row.

'It might take me a few minutes to get out of this suit, but I'll be there. Have no fear about that.'

Inside the main hall, Rex took his seat and patiently waited for the spectacle that was about to follow. A partially-constructed wall, with an incomplete mid-section where the band were set to perform, was already in position on stage. During the gig a team of roadies, hopefully fresh smelling, were going to place dozens of 3-foot cardboard 'bricks' into position, filling the remaining gaps in the wall. This enormous barrier would run the full width of the 160-foot stage, reaching an imposing height of some 40-foot on completion, and by the close of the first half, it would totally separate the band from the crowd.

The concert was simply breathtaking, and the sound was truly incredible. There were inflatable characters, animated videos, a crashing plane and of course the band, right there on stage. *(albeit behind a large cardboard wall)*

Roger controlled the show with his awesome persona. Nick and Rick were sensational, and when David appeared above the fully constructed 40-foot wall to play the legendary **Comfortably Numb** guitar solo, the whole place erupted.

As a direct result of the dedicated practice that morning, Bradley and Rex were absolutely note perfect performing on their air apparatus.

You've just got to put in the time; that's all there is to it.

The climactic ending of the concert saw over 300 cardboard boxes, painted like white bricks, pushed to the ground in a piece of theatrical symbolism. It all sounds a bit daft, but it was actually highly entertaining.

After the show had finished, as Rex went to leave, he was approached by an attractive young blonde woman.

'Are you a musician?' she asked. Obviously she had spotted the tremendous talent of the performers on the stage **and** the two special individuals in the front row.

'No, I'm an actor,' replied Rex, politely, in his usual shy and awkward manner.

'Really? I love actors, and I just love your accent…my name is Lucille.'

'LUCILLE?'

Rex looked horrified. No, she couldn't be. The name Lucille could easily be shortened to Lucy.

'But all my friends call me Lola.'

'Can I call you Lola?' asked Rex.

'Sure.'

A silver-tongued-fox of a conversation meant that Rex and Bradley could leave the smoking ruins of a cardboard wall behind them - joined by Lola.

It just goes to show, if you want to be discovered, you have to get out there and sell yourself.

Chapter 40 – After The Wall Came Down

Tuesday 12th February 1980

Following the triumph of *The Wall* shows, Rex felt enthused about life again. After several months of depression, he felt as if he had finally turned a corner and was settling into his new surroundings.

However, Rex was a British Citizen from overseas, whilst Bradley was an American Citizen living in his own country. This meant that Bradley could stay indefinitely in the USA, whereas Rex could not.

Bradley said that he knew someone who could help Rex out, no questions asked, and although Rex was reluctant to do anything illegal, he was feeling desperate.

Mel's Diner on Sunset Boulevard is a true 24-hour food paradise. It also makes one of the best vanilla milk shakes in Los Angeles. Rex had at least made that discovery in the short time since he'd arrived. It was there at 1pm, that Rex was scheduled to meet Bradley's contact.

Having arrived early, on account of having nothing to do, Rex was in a booth by the window with a vanilla shake on the table. It was about 12.40pm when he noticed a large man enter the diner. He must have been about 6-foot, 5-inches tall and as wide as the door. He was possibly one of the biggest men that Rex had ever seen. Thick black hair completed an impressive profile, and he was walking towards Rex.

Hang on !!!

'Roy?' blurted Rex, surprised to see Bradley's father.

'Finally!...It's only taken you 13 years, but we got there in the end. How are you, Rex?'

'Good thanks, I didn't recognise you.'

There was something different about Roy, and Rex couldn't place it.

'Yep, got rid of the old cookie-duster,' said Roy, rubbing his freshly shaven top-lip. 'You like it?'

'You look much younger...yes, I do like it.'

'What are you doing here?' asked Roy as Rex sat totally mesmerised by the streamlined look of his favourite assassin.

'Bradley told me to come and meet a contact here. I need to get a visa to stay in the States. I simply can't face living on my own in London...not without...well, you know what I mean.'

'How do you get a visa in a diner, Rex?'

It was a good question.

'I have no idea to tell you the truth. That's apparently why I'm meeting the contact here at one o'clock. It's all Bradley's idea, not mine.'

Roy said nothing and put his hands on the table. One big set of clubs they were too.

'Do you know what I do for a living, Rex?' said Roy, staring intensely.

Rex didn't think it was polite to say: *"kill people"*, so he was trying to think of the perfect *Embellishment* to make it sound more like a public service.

'I fulfil contracts, that's what I do. Now I'm here to fulfil one on you.'

'Fulfil contracts? No Roy, NO! Not now, I haven't finished my…'

The Chain had stopped mid-flow. It wasn't working properly. Rex tried again…

'This is a set-up! He's going to beat me with those giant hands, he…'

That was as far as Rex could get, either he had lost his touch, or the doom-o-meter was malfunctioning. Maybe it was the combination of wearing shorts in February, a vanilla milk shake on the table and the spectacular *Wall* concert that had affected his outlook on life. Three big positives right there.

'The Chain of Doom' as a mental condition had finally been broken. Hip Hip Hip…Hooray!

While the chain was snapping, Roy slid a business card across the table. Rex picked up the card, scanned it quickly and noticed three key bits of information:

➊: Roy Milwee

➋: Senior Director of Legal Affairs

➌: Warner Brothers

??? **Rex was confused.**

'You see, Rex. I'm a major player at Warner Brothers. We have enormous influence in music, television and films. It's a large international company, and that's why I was working in London.'

This was a day of enlightenment. It was about to get better...

'I'm the one who tipped Crispin Hansen off about how talented you are. I've negotiated contracts with Crispin before, many times, so I asked him to help you out. I told him that I loved you like my own son...and I still do.'

Revelation 1...Next...

'I also know a lot of people in band and venue management, so I find it easy to get premium tickets to premium events... like Pink Floyd shows.'

Revelation 2...Roy was on a roll...

'And I'm twenty minutes early. **I am your contact Rex.** I'm going to sponsor you for an O1 visa...do you know what that is?'

Revelation 3...Strike! Didn't even see one of those coming.

Rex was dumbfounded and shook his head to declare that he didn't have a clue about any such visa.

'An O1 is given to those people with extraordinary talent; it's the perfect visa for actors and musicians. Uncle Sam wants to get his hands on their fat, juicy tax dollars.'

In the 13 years that Rex had known Roy, he'd never heard him speak so much. Now he was faced with a dream scenario. With Roy's help, Rex could stay in LA with Bradley and avoid a dreaded return to London. In addition, Roy was a major player in the television and film industry. He was a friend with immense power and connections. Blimey!

Rex sat in silence as he struggled to digest three huge and unexpected revelations, all of which made sense looking back. Terry, the psychotic marksman, knew Roy because he wanted to be an actor, not because he was an underworld henchman. Roy wore a trench coat, not because he was on some top secret undercover work, but because it was a fashionable garment enjoyed by many in the 1970s.

It all made sense, all the pieces of the puzzle fell into place.

Suddenly, Rex became aware of a voice by his side…

'Anozer coffee, Monsieur Rex?…Monsieur???'

Chapter 41 – A Seaside Café (Reprise)

June 2005... (Part 2)

'Anozer café-crème, Monsieur Rex?'

A solitary voice had disturbed his journey through time, and Rex hadn't moved from outside the Levoilier Café in France.

(What happened after Rex met Roy in Mel's diner back in 1980? What other adventures did Rex have in The Hollywood Years leading up to this very moment, some 25 years later? Well, that's another story…)

After an earlier phone call from Crispin, with the shocking news of a Pink Floyd reunion gig, Rex had spent his morning gazing out over the tranquil bay of Cannes. The distant Esterel Hills had proven a useful focal point as he remembered his life back in England and his memories associated with the band.

This was a life Rex had never intended to leave behind, but the trauma of his break-up with Lucy had made living alone in London unbearable. America had provided the perfect sanctuary from an inner torment, and a short-term trip swiftly turned into an extended stay.

Rex had always wondered deep in his heart, if he would ever see his beloved home city again. Yet, by having vowed never to return to Britain, he was bound by his public pledge. The honour code of *"not losing face"* was instilled in him by his martial arts instructor, Steve Brown. Women the world over, often refer to this condition as: *"stupid male pride"*.

Perhaps the only positive of growing older is that time and life experiences have a habit of mellowing the soul. One learns to appreciate the benefit of wisdom that only age can bring. Things certainly seem different looking back. What once brought a tear will, in time, bring a smile.

'Would you like a drink, Monsieur?' asked Heffel for the third time as he tried to take an order.

'Er…yes please, another coffee would be good,' mumbled Rex, still lost in thought, his gaze transfixed out to sea.

'Something on your mind, Monsieur?'

'Hmmm…yes, yes I guess there is,' replied Rex, rubbing his chin as so many men do when in deep thought. Maybe it's an unconscious male trait, but once that chin is resting in the hand, supported by an elbow on the table, a quick chin rubbing seems an entirely natural thing to do. Maybe it simply aids the thinking process or sends out a warning signal to passers-by: *Brain at work. Do not disturb.*

'Well?' enquired Heffel, in a tell-me-more tone of voice.

One of the more obvious pitfalls of being a nano-celebrity is the over familiarity that crosses boundaries. Maybe Heffel questioned all of his customers with such vigour, but somehow, Rex doubted it.

As Heffel was probably one of the few people in Cannes, maybe even the whole of France, who knew what Rex did for a living, the usual polite boundary between the waiter and customer had been broken. In Heffel's mind Rex was his new best friend, so now the curious waiter wanted to know exactly what was troubling his British brother.

'Well, I've just heard that Pink Floyd are reforming for some big charity gig in London,' said Rex, finally coming back to his senses and turning to look at Heffel.

'Fantastique…when?'

Heffel seemed excited by this ground breaking news. Rex wasn't sure if it was public knowledge yet or an inside, for your ears only, tip from Crispin.

'Saturday the Second of July.'

'OH NO!…I am busy zat day,' exclaimed Heffel, declining the ticket he hadn't even been offered. 'I am afraid you must go wizout me.'

'I don't know that I can,' said Rex, still torn by his inner conflict.

'No Monsieur, I insist!' replied Heffel, wagging an index finger. 'We will go to anozer concert, anozer day.'

Heffel was blissfully unaware of the real reasons why his new best friend was in such turmoil. Rex was in a quandary over whether he should return to London to see one of the greatest bands of all-time, certainly his favourite band ever. As Rex pondered his decision, a list of essential *'things to do'* started to form in his mind:

1. Spend time with Mr Handsome.
2. Go to see the Houses of Parliament and Big Ben.
3. Eat fish and chips covered in tomato ketchup.

4 - 14. Currently under construction.

Crispin had planted the 'home soil' seed in Rex's subconscious, and it was now growing wildly. Damn that Crispin - again! He was brilliant!!!

'I'm afraid it's more complicated than that,' explained Rex.

'Yes?' said Heffel, standing in a way that meant nothing but a fulsome response was going to bring a fresh cup of coffee to the table.

'Well something happened in London a long time ago that broke my heart, so I decided to start again somewhere else. I haven't been back since.'

'But you are happy now, yes? Your heart is mended.'

'Yes…things kind of worked themselves out…I guess.' Rex really should have sounded more convincing.

'Oh Monsieur, it is sometimes too easy to be trapped in ze past. To be truly free, you must live for today…well, zat is what I sink anyway.'

Rex based his life on the teachings of the greatest thinkers known in Roman history: Confucius, Hansen, Mueller and Hunzelbergerstraum. Who would have thought that these inspirational figures would all now be joined by a French waiter named - Heffel Sargoo.

This Gallic genius had just uttered something so profound, that Rex had butterflies in his stomach. Indecision started to subside, and his pulse began to quicken. Heffel could be right. How could Rex possibly forego the once in a lifetime opportunity to see the reunion of Pink Floyd? There would also be the added benefit of ticking off all those *'things to do'* in one trip back to London; not to mention a chance to watch some proper telly with no adverts on the BBC.

It was time to swallow some pride.

'You know, Monsieur Rex. I have been sinking…' said Heffel, pausing nervously at first, only to rapidly grow in confidence. 'Maybe you take my number, and…well, you know zis man in Ollywood who can 'elp me become a big star…NOT ze one who direct your last film, of course…is good idea, yes?'

What a *Schmooze!* The waiter's tactics were impressive. Rex had apparently assumed the role of Heffel's agent, all over a coffee. Now he could make a few phone calls on his new client's behalf and help secure him a multi-million dollar deal in Hollywood. Well that's how it went in Heffel's mind anyway. It was that simple. The Frenchman would be on location by the end of the month, have a fabulous home in the Hollywood Hills by October, and in rehab by Christmas. Voila!

'Look my British chum, I will show you I can act.'

'Okaaayyy...' replied Rex hesitantly, slightly uncomfortable at the prospect of a public audition at a seaside café. What followed was unlikely to be in the running for an Oscar, but it was at least entertaining.

"   " said Heffel, as the French mime artist finally escaped from the box that he had been trapped in all morning.

Rex looked closer at Heffel. Despite an enormous nose, he really wasn't a bad-looking chap. Tall, slim, twenty-eight or twenty-nine-years-old probably, with a rock solid barnet. His dark brown eyes suddenly took on a desperate look as he waited for a favourable review of his acting talents. Heffel certainly had confidence to ask for what he wanted, and Rex found himself warming to his blunt French charm.

Time to sugar coat a response…

'Maybe Hollywood's not quite right for you yet, Heffel. It's hard to leave your home country and your family. Believe me, I know all about it. Why don't you build your name up here in France first and then try Los Angeles some other time, maybe in a year or two.'

Heffel looked crestfallen by this luke warm review of his mime act. Rex had let him down in the nicest way he could while still trying to leave the door open for the future. He was gently trying to steer Heffel away from a career move quite possibly destined to end with him waiting tables in LA, probably for less money and almost certainly nowhere near such a lovely view as this one at Levoilier in Cannes.

The other thing to consider is that sooner or later, once based in LA, the French philosopher would no doubt be turning up at Rex's home to hang out whenever he felt like it. Rex would probably let him too, as long as he could play a mean air guitar.

Then...inevitably...Heffel would become a regular fixture in the cast of *Doctor Danger*. Before he knew it, Rex would have his car towed for parking in Heffel's private space and then he would be escorted off the set, complete with a shredded contract. The fickle world of television would salute its new French saviour, showering the amazing Dr. Jacques with gifts, as he basked in global acclaim.

Staring at Heffel, Rex was immediately touched by the sad look in the waiter's eyes. Some people get their kicks out of stamping on other peoples' dreams, but not Rex.

'Look, I know a fantastic agent in London with really good connections. Maybe he can help you out, okay? I'll certainly tell him about you when I see him.'

'Really? Oh, my friend. I knew you would 'elp me.'

Heffel was instantly transformed. One minute, he was a broken man; the next, a star in the making, ecstatic with hope. With his silent buffoonery, he had just taken a white knuckle ride on the rollercoaster that is an entertainer's life and survived a possible critical mauling.

Rex was passing the buck to Crispin, of course. A far better judge of talent with a far thicker contacts book.

'So you are going back?' said Heffel, suddenly realising the significance of the earlier statement.

'Thanks to you, I do believe I am.'

'Très bien! Zat is such great news. One café-crème coming up, on ze house.'

With that, Heffel merrily whistled his way inside to collect the finest cup of coffee France had to offer. *The finest* as it was about to be served by a happy French waiter, which in itself is something to behold.

Rex felt a warm glow inside. It was so much easier to help someone, rather than cruelly dismiss them as a waste of time. It was good karma, and Rex believed in karma as it had served him well all of his life.

Staring at his mobile phone, Rex nervously drummed his left-hand on the table. His palms became clammy, his mouth felt dry and the butterflies in his stomach had another quick flutter. The deep-thought-chin-rub had advanced to a tentative biting of the right-index finger, just above the mid-knuckle, and Rex wondered what to do next.

Rex looked at his watch. London was one hour behind France, so it must be 11.37am in England...

'Maybe I'll wait until after Handsome's had lunch,' thought Rex. *'What time does he take lunch anyway?...actually, if it's eleven-thirty-seven now, he's probably having elevenses…wonder if he's still got those ginger nuts?…mmm…I haven't had one of those in years, you know…they've got to be dunked in tea though, they're far too hard otherwise…come on Rex, concentrate, think harder…mmm…custard creams, the elder statesman of all biscuits…'*

Thoughts were running around Rex's head like a bionic hamster on a wheel. Why was this all so difficult? Why should he wait until after lunch or a mid-morning tea and biscuit break? It was a pointless delaying tactic. Imagine telling Heffel that he wasn't going back to London after all this. Rex would certainly have to pay for the coffee, and then he would receive a free lecture…perhaps even another mime performance.

'What's all this got to do with the price of fish?' thought Rex.

A seemingly bizarre thought, which could only mean…
Rex was having an attack of 'Fish Related Doubt' (FRD).
This is a condition so terrible, it means Rex will agonise again and again over one simple decision. Every likely scenario and outcome has to be taken into consideration. If at all possible, the various options should be mapped out on a piece of paper or two. Classic symptoms of this fishy curse include making excessive lists, mumbling, nervous twitching, night-sweats, over-thinking a situation, and general indecision. The FRD was triggered by Rex's fish-counter obsession and the trauma he once suffered deciding whether to purchase a Dover Sole or a piece of Cod. How can anyone possibly choose between a Dover Sole set off with lemons or a Cod wearing parsley? FRD is a far less aggressive form of 'The Chain of Doom' but is no laughing matter. Rex had a serious decision to make.

One thing was for sure though. Before he made any decisions, Rex always made a list.

'Plans that either come to naught or half a page of scribbled lines.'

An abstract riddle had come into Rex's head from nowhere, so now he had to think some more...

'Wait a minute, that's a famous quote...where have I heard that before? It's brilliant. Must be Shakespeare. No...wait...Tennyson? It's too high brow for The Sweeney...Hmmm...must be Tennyson. Yes, yes that's it! Well done, you've got it...that's definitely it... I think???...oh, I need some paper!!!'

'Christ on a bike!' exclaimed Rex as he went for the hand-rub down the face, moving from the top of his forehead to the base of his chin.

This truly is a lovely manoeuvre, only to be executed under moments of extreme duress. The nervous twitch, coupled with the inexplicable expression of exasperation, meant that Rex had reached the final phase of his FRD attack.

'Time...Dark Side of the Moon!' Rex shouted aloud as he solved the abstract riddle. That was it...that was where the quote came from - **Pink Floyd lyrics!** If ever there was a sign from upstairs, this was one straight from Nan as she made more fairy cakes in heaven's kitchen. It was all part of a greater plan. This had to happen. It was destiny. Miss this concert??? Not on your Nellie!

Rex's eureka moment forced him to sit bolt upright. He grabbed his mobile from the table in an action so decisive, it signalled that he had conquered all of his doubts.

Rex Roman had a phone call to make...

Chapter 42 – Raise The White Flag 🏳

June 2005... (Part 3)

Back in the offices of CH Entertainments, Crispin had spent the morning busily making use of the telephone. A phone in the hands of Crispin was actually more of a weapon than a communication device.

Armed with that weapon, Crispin could pretty well batter anyone into submission - including Rex. The agent only had to tap into the right weakness for victory. For Rex, 25 years of exile, Pink Floyd and a once in a lifetime reunion concert never to be repeated were just too much of a bombardment. It was time to raise the white flag and surrender.

Crispin had a smug look on his handsome face as he saw:

REX ROMAN Mbl

flashing on his mobile phone. He knew that he had probably said enough to win the battle of wills, and after nearly 30 years of friendship, Crispin understood the inner workings of his favourite client's mind.

'Hello Rex, what do you think then?'

Rex was excited. His decision had been made. On the front page of his newspaper, in the top right-hand corner, he could see an image of a Union Jack. Back in London, he would be able to see that flag flying high, in the land of his birth. His mind was 100% focussed; not a fishy doubt in sight.

Rex shouted three words Crispin had been waiting to hear for over 25 years:

'I'M COMING HOME!' ✈ ✈ ✈

Chapter 43 – Hot Dog Temple

Live 8 - Saturday 2nd July 2005, Hyde Park, London

To fully appreciate the scale of the *Live 8* concert you have to have seen it, either live, on television or on the DVD box set. If you haven't, go and see it, come back and then we'll talk.

If you haven't got time because you can't bear to tear yourself away from this exhilarating final chapter, then let's set the scene...

Hyde Park is to London, what Central Park is to New York. A giant recreational green space set aside for the good mental health of the cities inhabitants. It's a place where you can always go and relax, read a book, have a picnic or throw a Frisbee. The choices are endless.

One of those choices could be to hold a gigantic concert, to remind world leaders that the problems in Africa are still there, and these are problems that need solving as a matter of urgency.

As citizens, all we can do is continually support these events, donate money and therefore show we care. Pink Floyd, like so many other performers, were about to stand up and be counted. For that reason alone, they should be saluted.

However, Pink Floyd mean so much to their number three fan. So many key Chapters in the Life of Rex Roman seem to have intertwined with their music. So much nostalgia had been triggered by news of this band's reunion that the significance of this gig could not be overlooked.

This wasn't a concert for Rex. This was a homecoming!

Arriving at Hyde Park was an emotional moment for Rex. He was back in a place where he had enjoyed countless post-ice-cream snoozes, during the 1976 heatwave. Rex knew how to live the high life.

Crispin's crafty use of his extensive contact list had enabled him to secure some VIP passes. These much sought after laminates gave access to a glamourous world of wooden tables and chairs, where various celebrities were corralled together in an area called the 'Artist Garden'.

Paul McCartney & U2 opened the show at 2pm with a fabulous rendition of Sgt. Pepper's Lonely Hearts Club Band. They were the first act in a musical extravaganza packed with twenty-six of the finest bands and solo artistes the world had to offer.

With over 200,000 people crammed into the park on an overcast day, the atmosphere was electric. A few party animals were flying flags proudly above their heads, and it was amazing to see how many of these were from different countries. This was a truly global event, on so many levels.

The show organisers had decided to divide the crowd into two areas, partly for safety reasons. A series of metal crash-barriers, about 200-foot from the front of the stage, created a large semi-circle area *(Section A)*. Further back behind these barriers, were the sprawling masses stretching back as far as the eye could see *(Section B)*. All those attendees who knew the right people, including Crispin and Rex, were in Section A, otherwise known as the Golden Circle. This semi-circle was in effect: a VIP viewing area. It was also packed with loads of ordinary folks all looking for a good time.

Confused??? Then take a look at the diagram…

The Live 8 Concert Hyde Park, London - 2nd July 2005

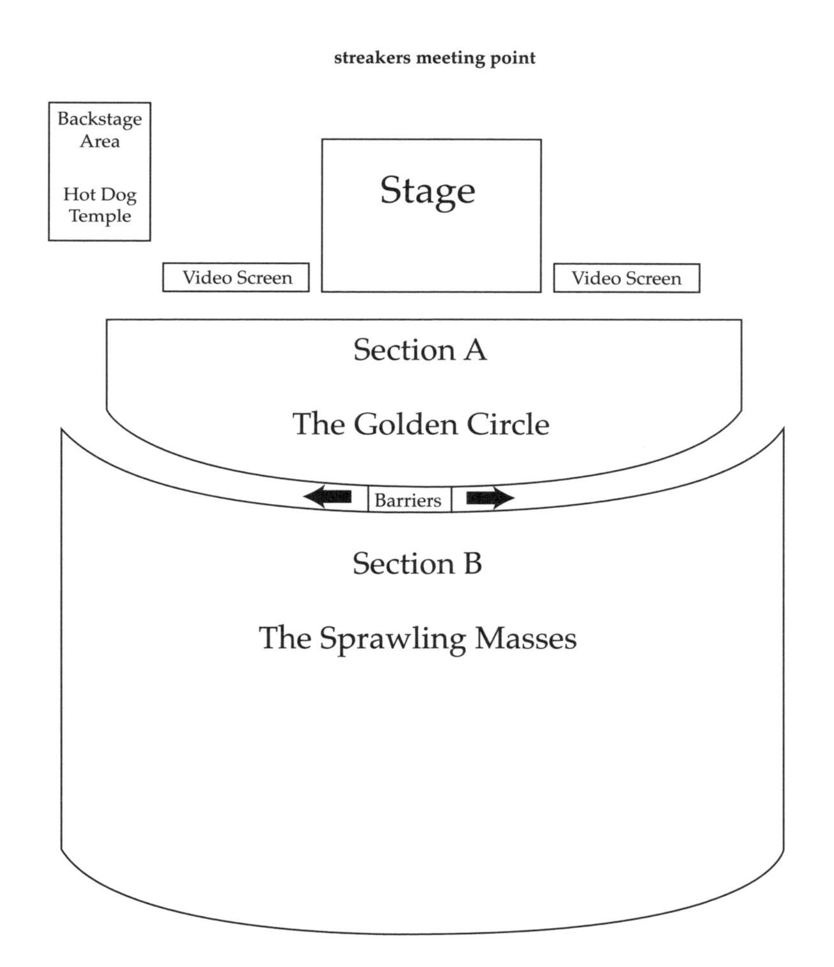

'Where are you going, Handsome?' shouted Rex as Crispin began walking off, only moments after Coldplay had finished their set.

A few fellow spectators near-by raised their eyebrows.

'I need a sit-down, my boy. I'm not as young as I was the last time you saw me.'

'Fair enough! I'll stay here.'

'That's fine, Rex. I'll meet you right here in an hour. If I can't find you and I'm not back by five o'clock, we'll meet by the hot dog stand in the VIP tent at six.'

'Okay, Handsome. See you later.'

The man standing next to Rex shuffled a few steps sideways. What a piece of luck! This gave Rex much more room to play air guitar, his new air bass and to practise his vastly improved air drums. Having met a drummer in Los Angeles who had given him some lessons, Rex now had his first big gig on his gargantuan air drum set. He definitely wouldn't be playing air saxophone though, that would be just plain daft.

When Elton John sang the alternative British national anthem, Saturday Night's Alright For Fighting, Rex had to choose his instrument carefully. He was torn between playing the guitar, bass, drums or some honky tonk piano. Luckily, a few other middle-aged-air-maestros moved closer to share the musical duties and joined him in his newly formed band.

Rex was back in London, and he was loving it.

As promised, Crispin returned after his one hour rest. He was impressed to see that Rex had been networking with the locals in his absence. Despite a ban on the sale of alcohol in the park, nothing was going to stop this party. Rex's excuse for his enthusiastic enjoyment of the day was the comfort of being back amongst his fellow countryman.

'Who's he?' asked Rex as some fat bloke from Reading did a stupid dance on the stage.

'Ricky Gervais, he's a comedic genius of our time,' explained Crispin. 'Look at the man move. Hilarious.'

Rex watched the dance. Obviously Ricky had been at Helen's wedding in 1978, and somehow he'd stolen all of the moves. He was a genius!

By this time, the show was already running late. Rex had carefully planned the day but skilfully adjusted his schedule to account for the delays. He made a decision that 10pm was the exact time to go for a hot dog, just before Pink Floyd were expected to go on. That way it would be like the old times: extra onions, ketchup, the whole gourmet selection and then... **Pink Floyd!** Rex couldn't imagine a more perfect day.

Crispin agreed with these arrangements, and while REM made many in the audience weep with their tear-jerking hit, Everybody Hurts, the agent went into a typing frenzy on his mobile phone. Having cornered a few famous faces during his rest backstage, he was now moving in for the 15% kill: his phone nearly melting under the strain of some frenetic finger work.

(You may think, as we conclude this tornado of time travel, that Rex is slightly on the heavy side given his liking for sweet stuff and high calorie snacking. You would be wrong. Rex is blessed with a gene which means that he can eat whatever he wants to and still stay slim. Sickening isn't it!)

The main advantage of the VIP passes meant easier access to refreshments, yet every time Rex went backstage he resisted the purchase of a hot dog. He would savour the experience later. He had will power and wasn't going to buckle until the agreed time, when he would gorge on certainly one, possibly two of the meaty treats. On one particular trip backstage, Rex bumped into an old friend…

'Dick?…Dick, is that you?'

'Hello Rex…well, well, I don't believe it. How are you?'

'I'm fine, thanks. Fancy seeing you here, it's a small world.'

'What are you doing with yourselves these days? Still acting?'

Normally questions like these call for the time honoured skills of the *Embellishment* to be rigorously applied; but maybe standing in line for the gents toilets isn't the best place to talk such rubbish.

'I live in the States nowadays. I've come home especially to see the Pink Floyd reunion. What about yourself? You still inspecting tent pegs?'

'Health and safety, Rex. It's the future of entertainment.'

Dick and Rex had first met on the set of *Auf der Flucht* in Berlin, back in 1979. They had become friends during the filmshoot and kept in touch when they returned to England. It was pure fluke that they happened to run into each other in Hyde Park; slightly uncomfortable that it happened to be in a queue for the toilets. Like a veteran *Schmoozer*, Dick slipped Rex his business card and asked him to call later in the week, so they could 'do lunch' and catch up.

The day lived up to all expectations, with many bands and international superstars plying their trade on stage. Out in the crowd, Rex and his new air band excitedly played along, seamlessly switching between instruments like the masters of rock that they were. Crispin was highly amused. As the light started to fade over Hyde Park, an important announcement was made...

'Okay, it's ten-to-ten, Handsome. Let's go!' said Rex, looking at his watch, keen to make his appointment with flavour.

Crispin and Rex headed backstage like men on a mission. There was a slip-way to the left of the stage which allowed easy access to the hallowed turf behind. Once there, Crispin thought that he'd seen a client, so he made his excuses and left Rex inside the VIP marquee. Never one to pass up a work opportunity, the agent decided to disappear for a couple of minutes to engage in some meaningless chit-chat. Rex couldn't be bothered with any dull *Schmoozing*; there was far more important business to attend to...

Approaching the catering area, one solitary man wearing a bright red baseball cap was all that stood between a salivating unemployed actor and a culinary sensation.

'Hot dog with extra onions, please,' said Rex, relieved to finally place his order.

'Here have mine, I can't stand them,' stated the man in the baseball cap, removing his hat and offering a gift.

Rex couldn't believe his ears. First, there was the generous offer of a *free* hot dog. Then the even more unbelievable statement, that this man didn't even like the nutritious snack in his outstretched hand. Yet it was a third thing that really caught Rex's attention...

'BRADLEY!!! I can't believe you're here,' gasped Rex in amazement.

'Hey buddy…you know CH, he's the best there is.'

Rex and Bradley nodded in acknowledgement of some supreme skills, before embracing in a man-hug as a smiling Crispin arrived at the stand. This was a set-up all along, secretly planned by the recognised master of smoke and mirrors. His well-meaning intention was to get the boys back together to see their favourite band.

'Mr Handsome…how do you do it? I am in awe yet again.'

'If truth be told my boy, I did it for me as much as for you. This is a momentous day for all of us. I wanted to share it with the people I love.'

If you measure your wealth by the cut of your friends, then Rex knew he was the richest man in the world. Crispin and Bradley had both been so pivotal in Rex's life, it was fitting that they were present to share the day.

'Here you go, mate,' said the hot dog vendor, handing Rex his snack.

'Thanks very much. Guys, take a look at this…TWINS!' gushed a proud Rex. 'How can today possibly get any better?'

'Would you like some ketchup with those?'

Rex was stunned by this question. This wasn't Crispin or Bradley; it was definitely a female voice. Rex discounted the impossible but still felt a tingle in his stomach like a sixth sense. He turned to his right, and there, stood with a ketchup bottle in her hand, was Lucy.

Rex was so shocked; he couldn't even speak at first. He stood trembling, with his jaw wide open.

'Hello Rex…remember me?'

'Yes…every single day of my life,' came the faltering reply.

Rex immediately dropped his two hot dogs and grabbed Lucy in the world's biggest cuddle, shattering all previous records, nestling her tightly under his chin. This was no time to hide feelings or shy away from a public display of affection. This was a reunion with a long-lost love. They were both older and wiser, but an instant magical connection was still there.

'Rex, I am…' whispered Lucy as she started to get some air in her lungs, once the vice-like embrace had slackened.

'Shhh…please don't,' said Rex, holding a shaky finger gently against Lucy's lips. 'Whatever happened has gone. We can only live for this day.'

Heffel was right. His wise words had been taken on board and quoted in the most appropriate situation.

Bradley and Crispin wiped tears from their eyes; such was the overwhelming emotion of the moment. The relentless march of time waits for no man and claims so much in its path. Yet, as these four special people huddled tightly in a group hug, it seemed to make time itself stand still, possibly even reverse.

They were all back together…at last.

For the first time in over 25 years, Rex felt whole again. Back in the presence of the three people who knew him best, he felt a sense of complete inner peace. It may only last for this one day, but it was a moment he would always treasure.

Holding hands, Rex and Lucy walked out to watch the greatest band the world has ever seen play a song that had stayed with them both for all those years…

WISH YOU WERE HERE

So Remember This

If you find yourself missing someone you love now or maybe even once loved in the past, and you are not with that special person - do not be sad.

They are alive and well as they live in your heart and in your mind. They are always with you. All you have to do is sit down and take the time to look.

As for what happened to Rex, Lucy and Bradley between 1980 and up to the *Live 8* concert, well that's another story. Where does it all go after the reunion???...well, that's another story too I guess.

But then for Rex Roman, things always did come along in 3s - didn't they?

A Final Thought

You may well think this is a load of old nonsense made up for fictional entertainment, but please think again. Next time you are renting a film, have a look for anything by German director Frederick Hunzelbergerstraum, from 1979 onwards, and you might just see Rex appearing in it.

Check the historical data against any number of Pink Floyd books. Listen to the band's music and lyrics. Go to see some of the locations mentioned, most of them still exist. Read this whole book again, and it will all seem totally different the second time around.

Do pigs really fly? Is this really fiction? You decide…

Dedicated to Tina

without whom this book could never have been made

GLAD YOU WERE HERE

Dedicated to Jenny,
Kate & Teddy...

and especially Nan

WISH YOU WERE HERE

Now for more... 

REX ROMAN Career List

~~ROCK 'N' ROLL STAR~~

~~WINE EXPERT~~

~~BEER TASTER~~

~~DOCTOR~~

~~A LIFE IN THE ROYAL NAVY~~

~~MERCHANT SEAMAN~~

~~PIRATE~~

~~FIRST BRITISH MAN IN SPACE~~

~~INTERNATIONAL PLAYBOY~~

~~DETECTIVE~~

ACTOR!!!!!!!

REX ROMAN Snooze Excuses

Allergic reaction to alcohol

Altitude sickness recovery

Medicinal (covering vast range of ailments, inc Food Poisoning)

Bravely advancing scientific research

To focus on my character

(More available on demand)

REX ROMAN Secret Shame List

1. Looking at the fish counter for too long in the local supermarket

2. Distracting security personnel and thus nearly causing a catastrophe over London

3. Playing air guitar without first correctly securing the stage area

WYWH Autograph Area

As greedy producers are dreaming of turning this book into a spectacular stage production called:

Wish You Were Here (WYWH)

these few pages have been left for you to collect your autographs from the cast.

Rex Roman has made a special request that the cast agree to do a 'meet and greet' after the show and talk to the audience, as he did when he first started acting. The cast will gladly sign this book and any other bits of reasonably priced 'official' memorabilia you may care to purchase.

REX ROMAN　　　　The LOVELY LUCY

WYWH Autograph Area

CRISPIN HANSEN

BRADLEY MILWEE

Any other assorted cast members

WYWH Autograph Area

The Band:

The Incredible Guitar Players

The Keyboard Gurus

WYWH Autograph Area

The Bass Rhythm King

The Delightfully Fragrant Backing Singers

WYWH Autograph Area

The Extremely Talented Multi-Instrumentalists

The Drummer

(A miracle if he can read, let alone write...try your best!)

A Message From REX ROMAN

Not Convinced I Even Exist???

Take a look at the excellent book 'Echoes' by Glenn Povey.
www.mindheadpublishing.co.uk
(It's the only Floyd reference book you need)

Look at the Brain Damage Website dedicated to Floyd.
www.brain-damage.co.uk

These two Floyd fact-and-photo libraries will convince you that everything happened on all of the dates given in this book. So, that's a start.

Next, most of the locations mentioned in this book are all still there. The more you look, the more you will believe. Sadly, I honestly was that comfortably dumb.

This book really is my story, embellished by one man over too much coffee. The Marathon bar didn't actually come out until 1973, or change its name to Snickers until 1990, but the embellishment was so funny, I had to let it go. The truth is that Bradley and I shared a Mars bar before the Kung Fu class, but we both loved Marathons.
(See Chapter 8)

Please DON'T pass this book around.
It's killing music, don't let it happen to books too.

If you enjoyed this book then please, please spread the word. The more books we sell, the more likely they'll make the stage show. I know that's the reason why Simon especially wanted to write my story in the first place.

Hope to see you again
Rex

Author Acknowledgements

A great many thanks are owed to so many people for making this book finally come to life. I would like to thank all of them personally for their support at various times.

Tina Lewis for her editing skills and fabulous artwork. Glenn Povey for his valuable input and wise advice. Dick Tee for his friendship and continued faith in WYWH. Kevin Bulford, Phil Page & Phil Clark at Ash Bash Music for keeping the business running while I flounce around writing all day. Andy C for maintaining my website & the typesetting tips *(I ignored)*. Michael Allen for recording the music. Starbucks for the countless tall vanilla lattes, no foam, that I shamefully consumed while I was thinking/working.

The honour roll: Phil Baker, Gerard McDonald, Fiona Ford, Kevy Canavan, Jill Schoonjans, Joe Orban, Dan Barraclough, Matt Johns, Bruce Tippen, Gary 'Boss' Summers, Gary Poole, Steve Hollister, Simon Livingstone & all those at Griptech TV, Dean Westall, Mike & Samantha Hartnett, Addy van der Borgh, Ben Challis & Harbottle & Lewis for all their legal advice. Kate Watkins, Paul Loasby & of course to Nick Mason for his kind letter wishing me luck. That gesture meant so much.

Finally thanks to Rex himself for being such an important inspiration to me and for the Kung Fu/air guitar lessons.

If I forgot anyone then I apologise, but it's been a long day. If I bored anyone along the way by banging on & on about WYWH/Rex Roman, then I thank you anyway for listening to me without calling the police.

Thank you all
Simon

Blank Page For Readers List

Top Rex Tips To Remember:

Blank Page For Readers List

Places Visited In The Book:

Blank Page For Readers List

Songs I Need To Practice On My Air Guitar: